ALICE C(

April 7, 1909

Alice Cobb was born and reared in Seymour, Indiana. Soon after graduating from Western College for Women in Oxford, Ohio, she began a long association with Pine Mountain Settlement School, Harlan County, Kentucky, as a teacher, community worker and board member. In a career spanning more than half a century, she was editor of *Mountain Life and Work*, a publication of the Council of Southern Mountain Workers based in Berea, Kentucky; director of Fourth Place Community Center (Congregational Italian Mission) in Brooklyn, New York; a community organization consultant in the Kentucky State Division of Child Welfare; and professor of Church and Community at Scarritt College, Nashville, Tennessee. During the Civil Rights movement she was a volunteer at Highlander Folk School, Monteagle, Tennessee, helping with literacy programs which prepared people to meet voter registration requirements in the South. Her many books for and about children received national attention in the mid-1900s. She received a Master of Arts degree from Union Theological Seminary in New York and a Doctor of Philosophy degree from Boston University.

MIRACLES AT PORTICI
Stories of Casa Materna

Also by Alice Cobb

War's Unconquered Children Speak (1953)
Refugees from War (1953)
Commissioned to Serve (1955)
The Swimming Pool (1957)
Raising Cane on Huckleberry (1959)
Conversations on Christian Responsibility (1962)
Come to Shanta Bhawan (1963)
Debby and Don Find New Friends (1964)
Who is My Neighbor? (1964)
Fruit of the Land (1965)
Exploring Basic Issues With Young People (1980)
Old Tales for a New Day (1981)
"Yes, Lord, I'll Do It": Scarritt's Century of Service (1987)
A Tapestry of Service: One Hundred Years Along the Way In Church
and Community Ministry (1989)
Pushing for Life: The Edgehill Church (1991)

Posthumously
With Looking Upward: A Novel (2011)

MIRACLES AT PORTICI
Stories of Casa Materna

By

ALICE COBB

Edited by Celia H. Miles and Louis Miles
Preface by Louis Miles
Foreword by Ruth Pool Moore

STONE IVY PRESS

Cover photograph: The Beach at Casa Materna

ISBN: 978-0-9834717-8-3

For information about obtaining copies of this book please contact
       Director of Institutional Advancement
       Scarritt-Bennett Center
       1008 19th Avenue, South
       Nashville, TN 37212
       Telephone: (615) 340-7472
       www.scarrittbennett.org

Acknowledgments

Dr. Don Beisswenger, executor of the estate of Alice Cobb, generously gave permission to publish and distribute *Miracles at Portici: Stories of Casa Materna.*

Ms. Laura Wells protected and cared for Alice Cobb's unpublished manuscripts, including *Miracles at Portici: Stories of Casa Materna*, and consequently made possible their posthumous publication.

CONTENTS

Preface

Throughout her long career Alice Cobb devoted much of her time and energy to the welfare of children. Soon after her 1930 graduation from Western College for Women she joined the staff at Pine Mountain Settlement School in Harlan County, Kentucky, as a teacher and community worker. Twice she spent five years there, sometimes as a volunteer, sometimes as a paid worker, and for many years she was a member of the board of directors. She also served for three years as a community organization consultant in the Kentucky State Division of Child Welfare. For two years she was the director of the Fourth Place Community Center (Congregational Italian Mission) in Brooklyn, New York, which operated after school programs for "latchkey" children. Later, when she was a faculty member at Scarritt College in Nashville, Tennessee, meeting the needs of children was a major emphasis of her Church and Community classes.

It was her writing, however, that introduced a large audience to the plight of children. Her *War's Unconquered Children Speak*, based on her own travels and interviews with young people, told the stories of dozens of children in refugee camps from Lapland to The Holy Land just after World War II. During these months when she was collecting material for *War's Unconquered Children Speak* she visited Casa Materna for the first time and began listening to the children's stories. She visited the nearby refugee camps and the clinics established by Dr. Tiofilo Santi and heard children there recount their awful suffering as they tried to escape the cruelty of war, often on their own, without family or other adults to help them. From this first visit to Casa Materna and its sister child welfare organizations, she became a lifelong friend of Casa Materna and the Santi family. This, then, was the genesis of *Miracles at Portici*.

In the years after *War's Unconquered Children Speak* was published, she devoted much of her energy to telling children's stories, not merely their sufferings but their triumphs over adversity. One of her early books, *The Swimming Pool*, depicted a group of children motivating a community to build a swimming pool for the use of their entire multiethnic population. The book generally received high praise from national reviewers and was widely used by study groups in the churches. Similar success followed with *Raising Cane on Huckleberry* and *Come to Shanta Bhawan*, which portrayed children as activists bringing their communities together to effect lasting social transformation.

During these years Ms. Cobb was also writing curriculum material for churches. Her *Conversations on Christian Responsibility*, *Debbie and Don Find New Friends* and *Exploring Basic Issues with Young People* were produced for The United Methodist Church for use in children's classes in Sunday schools. She also completed a collection of myths retold from many cultures begun by Mrs. Sophia Fahs, the best known twentieth-century liberal religious educator, who died before finishing the work. *Old Tales for a New Day* was intended primarily for children, but it also attracted a great number of adult readers. A study guide made the book especially useful for church use.

Casa Materna, however, was one of her favorite places, and she returned to visit the children and the Santi family numerous times after that initial discovery in the late 1940s. On all those visits, some lasting several weeks, others only a few days, she spent much of her time with the children, listening to their stories, learning their past, sharing their dreams. She soon was recording the impressions they left with her, and these journal entries eventually became the foundation on which *Miracles at Portici* was built.

The stories are intimate portrayals of the children who found at Casa Materna an environment that would allow them to grow into responsible adults coping with complex problems in a complex society. The stories are told with such insight that they show readers the remarkable intelligence and courage and strength which children can manifest in their lives when they are loved as completely as were the children at Casa Materna.

Louis Miles

Asheville, NC
January 2014

Foreword

Even before World War II, Casa Materna, the Naples orphanage, and its founder were well known. Pastor Riccardo Santi, a Methodist minister, began the work by rescuing two small children selling matches in a cold Italian winter to buy food. Soon the pastor's home was crowded with more and more homeless children, until within a few years hundreds of children had been clothed and fed and housed in the newly acquired palace of the Prince of Monaco and educated in the orphanage school. After the property was damaged by World War II bombing, American soldiers, captivated by the children, volunteered their labor to help rebuild the place. Nurses, house parents, social workers and teachers came from many countries to assist the Santis.

By the time Alice Cobb became acquainted with Casa Materna in the late 1940s, two hundred children were living there, and the school was accommodating many more. From the secure home that the Santi family had provided, many former residents of the orphanage were already leading productive lives in trades and professions.

Alice Cobb brought a lively interest in children with her when she visited Casa Materna, and although she was close to the Santi family, she spent more time with the children than with the adults. She discovered that they could communicate despite the language barrier—their English was poor and her Italian was poorer. She sat at table with them. She learned their songs. She encouraged them to share their stories, the sad times and the happy ones. She cried with them and laughed with them. And when she wrote about Casa Materna, she wrote about the important people at Casa Materna—the children.

Casa Materna's residential program closed in 2003—just two years short of its one hundredth anniversary. There was a great deal more to the institution than the orphanage, however, for it had been reaching out to help the surrounding community in a variety of ways. As early as the 1940s the Santi family provided "extra-orphanage" services to its neighbors. After the Allies gained control of southern Italy in World War II, when great numbers of displaced persons poured into the area from other parts of Europe, refugee camps were established to provide shelter and food. Medical problems caused by malnutrition, exposure in all weathers and rampant communicable diseases were treated by physicians. Always, children received special attention from the Santis. As specific needs were met, many of these programs closed. Others survived.

Among the strongest of these surviving community service programs was Casa Mia ("My House"), located in Ponticelli, a high-poverty and high-crime neighborhood near Portici. Casa Mia continued to provide an after school program where in a safe environment children were provided help with homework, nutritious meals, and opportunities for physical exercise classes, singing sessions and Bible study. Casa Mia offered these services for decades, and they continued unabated years after Casa Materna closed.

A newer program, only a few years old, is located in Villaricca, another high-poverty, high-crime suburb of Naples. Imparare Giocando ("Learning While Playing") was begun by Rosaria Vincenzi, a former Casa Materna child, to provide after school care for about fifty neighborhood children who received elementary computer training, cooking lessons, guided athletic activities, help with homework and instruction in Bible. Imparare Giocando provided a safe haven for play and learning. Children were also afforded the opportunity to visit cultural centers and sights in Italy that, because of their poverty, they would otherwise have been unable to enjoy.

For many years Casa Materna was supported by Americans organized into The Casa Materna Society, which was very successful in attracting private donations and foundation grants.

More than a decade after Casa Materna closed, in the suburbs of Naples, the 1980 words of Senator Edward Kennedy from a different context still echo: "The work goes on, the cause endures, the hope still lives, and the dreams shall never die."

Ruth Pool Moore
B.A., 1965 and M.A., 1966, Scarritt College

Nashville, TN
January 2014

Introduction

There is in this world, now in 1966, an ever-widening circle of people who are members of the Casa Materna family. They are in Italy, for Casa Materna is there, and they are in England, and in Switzerland, and other parts of Europe. They are in America and some are as far away as Asia and Africa and Australia. But wherever they live, these people are better and happier, and more sure about this life and the next because they belong to Casa Materna.

And yet one might say that this remarkable institution is only a home for children! Two hundred live there, and another hundred or so come from the neighborhood and nearby Naples to attend school. School and home are located on Corso Garibaldi in the city of Portici, which faces the sea and crowds against Naples back to back. The children eat and sleep in a handsome building which formerly was the villa of the prince of Monaco. The palace sits squarely on a black lava sand beach, and looks directly across Naples Bay to Capri and Ischia.

Leeward, and some distance away, but clearly visible in any weather, that monster Vesuvius looms, recalling the destruction of two ancient cities, and threatening now the newer city of Portici. People say the "old man" is likely to erupt again any time.

Casa Materna was founded about sixty years ago—in 1905— by a Methodist preacher named Riccardo Santi. After his retirement Pastor Santi's son Fabio, a lawyer, was director of Casa Materna and also Mayor of Portici, until his untimely death in a tragic motor accident in the mid 1950s. Since then the home has been directed by Fabio's two brothers, Emanuele, a minister, and Tiofilo, a physician.

So why should those who know Casa Materna feel particularly blessed? And why have they been saying to each other as they happen to meet here and there in unexpected places around the world, "Somebody ought to write a book about the place!"

A good many people have tried to do that very thing, of course. Articles about Casa Materna have been appearing in periodicals and newspapers and story books straight along through the decades. Recently the Reverend Cyril Davey of London published *The Santi*

Story, a captivating account of the founding family. Dr. Davey portrays Casa Materna as a stream of miracles responding to abiding faith.

Indeed, it does seem to be so. From the miracle of its inception, through all the succeeding miracles of its growth and endurance, straight into the present time, this institution has witnessed to answered prayer and devotion rewarded. I confess, writing these words, to a feeling of betrayal against the unnumbered saints of this world, just as faithful as Riccardo Santi, just as intrepid laborers in the Lord's vineyard, whose faith and works have seemed not to have been so rewarded, and whose prayers have apparently been answered by an everlasting *no*, instead of *yes*. Yet one cannot read or hear the story of Casa Materna without being infected with some kind of belief in purpose and direction for our troubled world.

Here, then, it stands—intact six decades on—veteran of two world wars, bombed, evacuated, destroyed, evicted, re-occupied and finally rebuilt, housed in a royal palace. And here are today's children of Italy, and other countries, too, playing in formal gardens among fountains and marble gods and goddesses carried out of Pompeii when that ruined city was dug up out of the lava. Here are the flowers blooming, as they always have, and here are the children, singing. Their songs are songs of joy, and—let us never be deceived—these children persist in thanking *God*!

So Casa Materna is more than just a home, and it is home for more than just these two hundred children. It is for all those who know it, maybe, a little vacation from the wearisome temptation to despair. Here, for a little while at least, one can relax and believe in something. Here at Casa Materna God is not dead but very much alive, and here for some obscure reason of his own, He has elected to say *yes*.

The purpose of these stories is not to offer another biographical historical study, although the past needs to be recalled for the very work's sake, but to present some "true life" stories about the experiences of some of the children who have been at Casa Materna.

In order to prepare for writing the stories I went back to Italy, after being several years away, to be reminded again of past wonders and to be assured that they continue today. I was not disappointed. The home is still deep in its original business of restoring life and happiness to children, and re-uniting broken families. I was impressed especially with what has never changed. Casa Materna's therapy has always been summed up in faith and loving care. The medicine of love is continuously prescribed and administered in giant doses, not only for children but for all who visit. Casa Materna remains that kind of place.

And now, with a sheaf of notes and a crowd of memories, and with my diary before me, I find myself seething with stories to tell and not quite sure how to tell them. A few things are certain, however. I have determined to write nothing which would hurt or demean any child. Even in my notes the names are changed, but every boy and girl described has been at Casa Materna. The facts, even those which are better made into fiction stories, are true. Most of the children I met knew the purpose of my recent visit. All of the Santi family and the staff knew and helped me in every way they could. Aware that the eyes of all are upon this mission of mine, I can only trust that their encouragement will make of it a good report and true.

Alice Cobb
Nashville, Tennessee
1967

1. Return to Casa Materna

The introduction to Casa Materna's new world of problems began for me at once, with the airport trip. Our Fiat ride through the center of Naples and out to Portici appeared to be a breathless test of skill and daring, as we wove in and out of endless snarls of other little automobiles chasing each other up and down and across the streets, mufflers wide open, horns screaming, and all of us jamming together at the intersections. Naples had always been a little terrifying to me, but I could not recall it ever before being so aggressively busy. I looked for red and green lights, but the driver told me there were very few in the city.

"You should remember that Neapolitans are individualists," he said. "They don't take orders."

There was an awkward moment when I suggested stopping at the big railroad station, which suddenly hove into view only a few yards away. But looking across the sea of cars and trucks and buses to be untangled and maneuvered through, we decided unanimously that a train schedule to Rome was hardly worth the effort.

"Only a few short steps, but an hour to get there," the driver said, reading my mind. "Time and space are all mixed up here, only we have maybe more time than space!" Of course he was joking, but he had a point. "You'd hardly know you aren't in New York, I suppose," he went on. "Does it feel at home here?"

The central part of the city did have a New York look, with enormous department store windows displaying modish, handsome and expensive goods. The small shop quaintness I remembered had given way in metropolitan Naples to urban efficiency. Prices were higher than at home, and the clothes were better looking, too, I thought. Women shoppers were well-dressed and coifed—and these were not American tourists, either. Italy and the Italians seemed to be doing all right.

The driver pointed out to me the new highrise public buildings, the ultramodern apartment dwellings, the OMEC stores which are the Italian version of our Woolworth and Kresge chains, and the great glass-front post office, Mussolini's monument in southern Italy.

I didn't begin to get the old time Naples feeling until we passed a funeral cortege with six horses pulling a massive, ornate hearse, and a crowd of fifty or more men walking behind. The procession was in odd contrast with the impersonal crush of motor traffic all around it, but the horses seemed undisturbed, and I had a moment of something like reassurance. In death, anyway, life began to take on some personal meaning, and a horse leading a funeral could cope even with urbanization.

"It must be the funeral of a man," the driver said. "There were no women walking with them. It's an old custom. And there were six horses. The funeral was middle class!"

There were landmarks that I had known well in other years. There was the church were Pastor Riccardo Santi had begun his mission in Naples, the house where the family had lived in the early, struggling times, and the archway in the center of the city where some sixty years ago the pastor had discovered the first two homeless children selling matches.

But all these places had to be pointed out to me in the new Naples. Now souvenir venders hawked everything from cameos to clay images of Vesuvius, and the old archway was a busy market place. Newsstands on both sides carried papers from all over the world, including Nashville, Tennessee, I was told. The old was everywhere dwarfed and shouted down by the rush of today's business that engulfed the new Naples.

"It is progress," the driver explained. "It is happening all over Italy. Big business. Jobs. Profits."

"Is it happening farther south?" I asked. I found that hard to believe. "Toward Brindisi? And Calabria?"

"Farther south it is not so good as here," he admitted. "But it is better than before. In my village, which is Petrona in Calabria, there is one bathroom now. And there is an electric factory. It is not good, you might say, but it is better."

There is another side to the progress picture, however, even in Naples, and I did not entirely miss it, even on that first ride.

In Italy, as in America, the rich are likely to be rich at the expense of the poor, and the voiceless response to prosperity for some is bitter poverty for many. It was always so everywhere, including Naples, and it is still there, less apparent now than only a few years ago, scarcely noticeable to the casual tourist. Behind the façade of new streets and handsome new shops and storefronts, in the narrow side alleys and courtyards off the main thoroughfares, the silent poor can be found. They are the same poor who have always been there, and increased national prosperity has touched them very little if at all. Progress has built a wall to hide the poor in the center of the town, but they are there, the "other Italy," and this other Italy is Casa Materna's concern. We plunged through that wall as we left the center of town and started out toward Portici.

Corso Garibaldi begins as a rather wide street in Naples, growing narrower and more crowded by the mile as it continues straight along into Portici. There is no way of telling where Naples ends and Portici begins except for the Christ statue with arms stretched out to separate these two cities. And here, at last, I began to feel on familiar ground.

This is the area which was shattered with bombs during the Allied conquest of Naples during World War II. Rebuilding has been slow. Even now, twenty years later, one sees whole blocks of sagging doorways, gaping windows overhead, and in some places stout wooden braces propped like buttresses against the crumbling walls to keep them from collapsing.

"Every year a few of the houses fall," the driver told me. "They are condemned, but what can you do? The people do not move. Would you tear down a building when people are living inside, with ever so many in a room?"

I asked why the people didn't move, if the buildings were condemned, but I knew the answer before it came. "There is no place to go."

One of the problems of this new Naples, and of the new Portici crowding against it, is the exploding population. More people are being born, more are coming from the south of Italy, more of the rural fringe poor are seeking jobs in the city, and more people are living more years. Housing projects are going up, and fairly fast, but there is not enough room, even if there were enough money, to build all that are

20

needed. For the lucky ones who can get places in the projects there is no preparation for the new kind of highrise living, and no help with adjusting to it. But for most of these people, there is not even a highrise to go to.

With all these thoughts filling my mind I was startled to find we had traveled the length of Corso Garibaldi and were drawing up before the great gate, number 235. Like everything else these days we were moving too fast for me.

But then once again, at Casa Materna, there happened the pleasant surprise of leaving the confusion of the narrow street outside, to look abruptly into the peace of a royal garden. Perhaps this single experience of calm after storm may be the shock that brings so many visitors back here time after time again. Perhaps they want to see if it can happen a second and a third time, just as it did before. It always happens!

The view through the archway into the garden looked much the same and the broad walkway stretching down toward the sea had not changed. The palms stood majestically in two lines. The same bougainvillea in gorgeous purple and crimson draped itself over walls on either side of the garden, and down at the end of the walkway was the great fountain I remembered, and even from the gateway I could see Neptune down there, still serenely holding high his ever overflowing pool of water. Background for it all was the red palace, and on either side of the palace there was a long look at the sea, hazy now in the early twilight. Casa Materna's Pompeian red color had turned to warm pink, and I could barely make out the words carved above the four great columns in front. But I knew what they were. "Lasciate i fanciulli venire a me," which means, of course, "Let the little children come to me."

The gatekeeper was the same, and I remembered him although he had forgotten me. At his nod we rode straight along under the oleanders and between the lines of palms, down to a wide patio beside Casa Materna's basement dining room, which used to be the palace wine cellars. Those walls are four feet deep.

The evening meal had already begun, and even from outside we could hear the sound of children's voices like bees humming, but higher pitched. As we opened the door the humming changed to a roar that filled my ears so that I strained to hear the greetings coming from both sides. I looked down the long room where the boys were enthusiastically scraping their plates, and then back to the smaller room on one side where older girls and nursery children were just as intent on theirs.

This was the very best time of all to have come, I thought. Dinner time at Casa Materna!

I was hastily thrust into a chair, shoved up to the big table in front, presented with a steaming bowl of soup and a plate of good, solid Italian bread. An instant later a dish of Parmesan appeared, to sprinkle over the soup, and I was at home again, at Casa Materna. While the din in the room was making any kind of talk impossible I had a moment or two to look around, to seek out the people who had been there before, to miss the ones no longer there.

The years had made a difference.

Pastor Emanuele was there, and Dr. Tiofilo. They had not changed very much, I thought. And their sister Louisa was there, also.

Fabio Santi was sadly absent, and Mama and Papa Santi. I recalled that on my last visit that Pastor Riccardo had been gone for only two weeks, and the posters on the wall outside still proclaimed his greatness, for in Italy, after a great man has died, it is customary to put up posters, so that all the world may know and pay tribute. There were new staff people, two from England, two from America, and a Swedish nurse. They were new, but they might have been the very ones who had sat around that big table years before. At Casa Materna, I remembered, faces might change, but the spirit stays the same, always. I could feel myself slipping back into the life here, so easily that it was as though I had never left it.

It was easy to slip back into the end-of-supper routine, too.

After a few days, visitors to Casa Materna soon learn that every evening of the world, there is a ritual that never varies. It is faithful, strictly Italian, traditional, regimented, sentimental, and appropriate. More than appropriate, it is essential in this place.

First, the big boys line up two-by-two, ready to march out through the side door. Just before they go, all stand at attention, appear

22

to click their heels together military style, and chorus, "Arrivederci!" Teachers, staff and visitors wave and call back, "Arrivederci!" Then, forward march, hup, two, three, four, and they are gone.

But this is not the end. The older girls now line up two-by-two by the main door, in orderly but not so army-like formation. They call out, "Arrivederci!" not quite so lustily as the boys, but with warmth, and they are answered, "Arrivederci!" These shouts of "Farewell and blessing!" fill the room.

But still the evening ceremonial is not finished.

Last of all, every evening, comes the warm, touching, slobbery moment that could be all wrong, but always turns out to be right. It is the time when, as Louisa Santi says, "The children come around." These are the least ones, nursery and kindergarten. They cluster about the table where the grown-ups usually sit, and then firmly and faithfully, one by one, they embrace everybody present. Nobody escapes, and nobody ever wants to. The children love it. In their enthusiasm some manage to get twice around the big table before leaving reluctantly to join their own haphazard line that means to be a double line but isn't, and goes straggling cheerfully out behind the big girls. They chirrup, "Arrivederci!" but I have an idea that their "Farewell and blessing!" is in Italian baby-talk.

That is all. Granted the ritual sounds in the telling a little foolish and unsanitary, yet evening after evening, year after year, it continues, waxing but never waning. Visitors soon recognize that there is a studied usefulness for the little ones in every motion. Newly arrived children, bound up and tight inside themselves, melt and relax and become comfortable in their new home, as if a door were opened to let them love and be loved. It is sweet, and fun, and therapy, and a part of the fabric of Casa Materna.

On this evening, newly arrived and still a stranger to them, I was caught up willy-nilly in a swarm of small arms and moist kisses. I noticed one little girl, especially, because she was outside the tangle, and with eyes for no one else but the pastor. I noticed her, too, because Pastor Emanuele said to me, "This is our Violetta. She limps a little. Notice her because she is a special child."

Apparently this was to be a story, perhaps the first of the stories from Casa Materna. I would remember Violetta and ask about her later.

But now, with all the children gone, and in the quiet that was settling around us, I looked at the people around me again, thought of the joyous confusion just passed, and wondered. I asked myself if all this evening ceremony which seemed so much like the old days could still be appropriate for the new times. I wondered what there could be in the timelessness I felt around me that could be relevant to that new Naples I had been in only a little while ago. I was convinced that what Casa Materna possessed was right. But why was all this, which was *not* new, still *new*?

I thought I knew the answer. Papa Santi had said a long time ago, "I do not ask if a child needs help—I become that child."

I knew I would continue to look for changes and would find them, but there would be a core of constancy, too, that would not need to be questioned—only understood and accepted, with gratitude.,

I felt ready for Violetta, and the others.

2. Violetta

As I look back now, every one of these simple reports seems to have begun for me in a setting steeped in symbolism, so that even quiet little facts about children were in danger of becoming sermons.

Several stories, like Violetta's, developed out of after-supper talks on the palace terrace that looks across Naples Bay. Evenings were long because it was never dark before nine or ten o'clock. Sometimes Emanuele Santi played on his violin. Now and again American battle ships came in our line of vision, or toy-sized sail boats silhouetted against what seemed like great shadows on the horizon, but were really islands, Ischia and Capri, or part-islands, like Pusuoli where St. Paul stopped on his journey from Malta and from where he probably walked the whole journey to Rome.

As it grew darker, and the lights appeared around the bay we could hear soft sounds of children's voices above and around us, talking, or singing, and I thought of contented noises chickens make in a chicken house at dusky dark.

One evening, several days after I had come, Pastor Emanuele reminded me of the little girl who liked to linger after the meal was over.

"Have you noticed her?' he asked. "The one who is slow to join the line to go out?"

I remembered her. Violetta looked to be seven or eight, although I learned afterward that she was ten. She was less confident than the others, but even more determined, too. I noticed that after dinner she clung to Pastor Emanuele's hand, refusing stubbornly to be pushed aside by the crowd. And after all the rest had gone she was still there with us. On this very evening she had lingered until he unclasped gently the unwilling fingers and directed her to the end of the line of children. Violetta limped along after them then, still looking back, and waving her hand until she was outside the door.

"You mean Violetta," I said. Of course I remembered her and that he had said to me that first night, "Notice her, because she is different."

"Violetta," he repeated after me, as though he liked the sound of the word. "What a beautiful child!"

That seemed to me a little extravagant. Violetta was attractive in a somber sort of way, I thought, but not beautiful as so many of the little girls were. Pathetic, of course, but not beautiful.

"She is close to my heart," he said to me. "I think you will like to know more about Violetta." He was quiet for a long moment and then nodded. "I have it. We begin with the night one week ago. We begin with that night, and you may go on from there."

A week ago? That was before I had come, and it seemed forever. I set my mind for the story.

"Well, I went to sleep early, almost as early as the children, and it was still light on the sea. But can you imagine I slept very little! Only half the night!" He looked unhappy remembering. "Because perhaps about midnight there was the most dreadful clatter on my door here." He nodded toward the window of his own apartment beyond the terrace. "I wakened at once, and feared for the children sleeping overhead. But I need not have worried." He smiled then. "They sleep hard, the little ones. There was not a sound from them."

"But the clatter that wakened you—" I began.

"It was the good wife of our gatekeeper, calling me to come quickly, to come at once, because there was an intruder at the gate."

"Did he break in from the street?" I asked. "Through that big iron gate?"

"Not *he*!" Emanuele corrected me. "*She*! The intruder was a woman. Well, I dressed as quickly as I could, and went up the walkway fast, and before I was even halfway to the gate I could hear the racket." He shuddered.

"It was a woman shouting, and there can be nothing more unpleasant to hear in the dead of night than the angry voice of a determined woman." He dismissed us all, determined or otherwise, with an impatient wave of his hand.

"That gatekeeper, poor soul, tried to find places between her complaints, for answering. He was telling her the little girl was asleep. *All* the children were asleep! But that woman would not be quiet. And then late as it was, some people out in the street came to ask what was the trouble at Casa Materna. We are known to be a quiet place." He shook his head sadly. "There is really nothing more unpleasant than a noisy, determined woman," he repeated.

"Who was she?" I asked.

"Well, it was difficult to find out," he said. "I had to learn from the gatekeeper. It seemed she had come demanding to see one of the children, but of course I said to her what the gatekeeper had already been saying to her. 'It is late at night,' I said. 'It is midnight. Time for children to be asleep and all of our children *are* asleep. To rouse one of them would frighten all the others and herself. They would hardly sleep again tonight!' I said to her."

"'But you do not understand!' she insisted, and this was the first time I had from her a coherent, sensible statement. For the first time I could see that woman in the light from the street, which is not very bright. She was young, with poor clothing, naturally, for our people are poor. She was handsome in a way. And she was a stranger. I had not seen that woman before.

"'Your child is here?' I asked her then. 'Are you sure? Perhaps the Catholic hostel on this same street—'

"She was sure. This was the place.

"'It is Violetta,' the woman said clearly at last. 'Violetta is my child and I must see her.'

"Well, of course I knew Violetta. I knew her very well. She had come a month before, with the police of Naples. But I had not seen this woman.

"'Violetta is happy,' I said. 'She is well. But she needs to sleep tonight. Come tomorrow, please, when you will not frighten her.'" He smiled ruefully. "You see how simple it is to tell another what to do! What a fool I was.

"But that woman said again, 'You do not understand.' And then she said, 'I have this night been released from prison. I have walked all the way. I came as soon as I could come.'"

Pastor Emanuele stopped speaking then, perhaps to let me feel the shock of what the woman had said.

"The prison is many miles away," he observed. "Such a long walk, to find her Violetta!"

I wanted to ask many questions, but waited, because he had planned the telling of the story carefully.

"It was all clear to me then," he said at last. "And what she said was true. Of course I had not understood. It was as simple as that. We went at once to bring little Violetta."

"You did allow her to see her little girl then?" I said. "And did you waken her?"

He looked shocked.

"But of course! Would you keep a woman from her child? When she was in prison, and had walked so far?"

"And was she frightened?" I asked.

"Of course!" he said, impatiently. "All of them were frightened. There was a great noise and confusion. But, you see, that woman had walked from prison to see her child. I had not understood!"

"Were they happy to be together again?"

"It is hard to tell you how happy!" he said simply. "Mother and child stayed together in that small bed for the rest of that night. It was not so long!"

That was how the story began for me, and the truth is that I spent a long time trying to decide what Pastor Emanuele meant when he kept reminding me that he had not understood. I puzzled over it for most of the rest of my time in Italy. But meanwhile I began to complete the story, and to piece it out, detective-story style. It came in small bits, from different people, and from Violetta herself, as I watched her every day grow a little brighter and happier, and even younger. As Pastor Emanuele says, a girl of ten can be much older than ten, but it is *wrong* for her to be older!

From the records in the office I learned some of the facts. They were put into my hands by Donatella, the attractive and efficient young secretary, who told me she was a "Casa Materna child," herself.

"I think you should know this fact," she said gravely. Her English was unusually good, and I learned that she had spent a few months in "Washington, D.C. I began to be sensitive to another story, behind the record about Violetta.

The record said that Violetta had been born in Naples, stricken with polio when she was seven, and almost but not quite cured. She

28

would bear a slight limp for the rest of her life. The father of this girl, said the record, was untrained, and young. He and his wife had tried a good many ways of making enough money to support themselves and Violetta, and the grandmother who lived with them. The room—just one room—where they lived was off a small alley that ran back of a great church and convent near the center of town. The family became steadily worse off, and after Violetta's attack of polio, they were not only poor, but deep in debt. When Violetta was nine, another child was on the way.

Then, printed in cold black and white, I read how Violetta's parents, being unable to make an honest living, became involved in some dishonest dealings with an electrical company, were reported by the grandmother to the police, arrested and imprisoned. The mother would be held for a few weeks only. The father, being the more responsible party, would be in prison for a longer period. Violetta had come to Casa Materna with the police officer. The new baby, still of nursing age, had gone with the mother to prison.

So efficiently a few lines of type can dispose of a tragedy in the lives of four people, or five, if the nursing infant counts.

I looked up from the half-page, single-spaced typing, to find Donatella watching me intently. It appeared that some response was expected of me. I wondered if she had typed that report herself and if I ought to tell her how I felt about reports.

"I wish I knew more," I began cautiously.

She dismissed my remark, and the record, too, with one swift gesture.

"Let me tell you what happened." she said. "May I tell you how it was?"

This is the story as Donatella told it.

"They were working as hard as they could, those two young people, and growing poorer and poorer instead of richer, and something *had* to be done," she said. There was a terrible urgency in her voice. "You would have felt the same way." she assured me. "Anyone would have done the same or much worse. That young man talked with some of his friends, and all right, they maybe gave him bad advice. He learned about a business selling electrical—what do you call them?"

I supplied, "Appliances."

"Yes, yes, appliances. Electrical appliances. They would take the iron or the toastmaker or whatever it might be from the company, and sell it for as much as they could get, and then pay the company. That was the business. They were supposed to make a profit."

"Of course," I agreed.

"Only it did not work out that way." She was a little hazy about the problem. "Perhaps they lost the appliances, or counted the money the wrong way. They were untrained, you see. They were not educated. Anyway, something happened. The company said they kept the money and then moved in order not to be discovered. But I think they were not good business people."

She looked me straight in the eye and spoke rather fiercely, I thought.

"I suppose an electrical company would hardly need the money for one toastmaker! And what does an electrical company know about hungry little girls and nursing babies? Nothing! Nothing at all!"

She apologized for being close to tears.

"You see, I know what happens to such people," she said. "Violetta is an honest child. There must have been a mistake!

"Perhaps there was a mistake. Anyway, the police came, found the shop empty, and went at once to find the grandmother, in the place where these people had lived.

"But she was *forced* to inform," Donatella exclaimed again. "Can you think what it is like to be questioned by the police of Naples? They have no mercy for the poor. There was nothing else for that grandmother to do."

And so the little family, four now, with the baby, were hunted and found without any appliances and without any money either. The parents and the young baby went to prison, and Violetta was brought to Casa Materna. Donatella explained that the police often brought children to the home this way, when there was no other place for them.

"I suppose she could have stayed with the grandmother, poor little one," Donatella said. "But how much that child does hate her grandmother! 'Traitor!' she calls her. 'Cruel informer!' Hate, hate, hate! Grandmother hates father. Child hates grandmother. Father feeds hatred of child. Father suspects mother. Child loves father and mother who quarrel with each other. Poor little Violetta, pulled by one and then the other."

"Can't anyone, *you* maybe, explain to Violetta?" I asked weakly. "After all, she is ten. Maybe she could understand."

Donatella shrugged her shoulders in a way that is distinctly Italian and may mean any number of things. This time it meant that I had asked a foolish question.

"Well, there are others here with that problem and more problems," she said. "You see, I am one with them. I know!"

The office interview left me feeling somehow reproved or reproached. I carried my questions to supper that evening, and Pastor Emanuele was deeply touched.

"She is right!" he said. "Donatella is right, and hatred is indeed a sickness. You see, the real tragedy here has not much to do with police or prisons or stealing electrical appliances, if they were actually stolen. The real problem is the damage to the family, and the burden that comes down upon this innocent child."

"But with the mother now out of prison—" I began, and hesitated, wanting to ask why Violetta was still at Casa Materna. In America, I knew, a child is hardly ever kept from its mother, if the mother wants it and can care for it.

"The mother would like to take her child," he admitted, answering my unspoken question. "And the grandmother would like to have them both. But Violetta is unwilling to go to them. The father's letters continue to come from the prison, you see. Hatred is a sickness."

"What will happen to Violetta, then?" I asked.

Pastor Emanuele shrugged in the Italian way, but sadly. My question this time was futile, perhaps, but not foolish.

"Who knows?" he answered. "The story is the kind that might have different endings. What do you call it in your country?"

"Open-ended," I said.

"Most of the stories around you here are open-ended," he said. "All I can tell you is that Casa Materna's work is to keep and love the child and, God willing, to restore the family to each other. But these things happen slowly. Very slowly. One grows impatient!"

We had been watching Violetta, there in the dining room. She seemed absorbed in her own thoughts at the table with the younger children. But as if a new idea had suddenly occurred to her she darted from her place, and ran to Pastor Emanuele, smiling confidently.

"She looks younger!" I said. "She really does look younger tonight."

"Ah, yes, younger!" He spoke as if he were considering the idea and then turned to talk to the child.

But for some reason she did not care to stay near him this time. A quick hug and she was on her way. She may have seen signs of tears in the pastor's eyes, for tears were there, and her own black eyes went wonderingly to his, as she left us. Then she was drawn into the group. It was clear that Violetta was one of them.

"I believe those little ones understand her," I said.

"Of course," Pastor Emanuele said. "It is easy to forget how they are all experienced in suffering. Even the least ones know how to be doctors."

"Doctors! To each other!" I exclaimed. It was a new idea.

"How else could they be cured?" he asked. "How could it be otherwise?"

Violetta turned to wave to him a special good-bye as she joined in the chorus of "Arrivederci!"

I said "Farewell and blessing!" under my breath. It seemed as good an ending as any for the open-ended story.

3. Georgio and the Doctor

This story and the one which follows are really from Casa Mia, which is a busy sister agency in the heart of Naples' slums. It is a neighborhood house, started by Dr. Tiofilo Santi soon after the Second World War, to help meet needs of the people who fled to caves outside the city during the bombing, and then flocked back into the ruined city after the war was over. When Dr. Tiofilo returned from the army he found this vast new problem in Naples and recognized it as Casa Materna's. But a home for children cannot spread itself to meet the needs of a refugee population. Furthermore, the refugees were not only the Neapolitans made homeless by the war. They were migrants from starving southern villages, and they were newcomers from Yugoslavia and Hungary.

Dr. Tiofilo organized three large refugee camps outside Naples for the migrants from other countries, and then he set up Casa Mia to try to deal with all the multiplicity of social as well as medical problems in the overcrowded inner city of Naples. Toynbee Hall of London was his model, and Casa Mia is still the only social center of this kind in Italy.

Each one of my visits to Naples had included a brief visit to the Casa Mia neighborhood, which is a streetcar ride along Corso Garibaldi out of Portici and into Naples. I have been impressed each time with the constant change, the increased numbers of people, and increasing poverty, apparent to the most casual observer. The population problem of Naples is matched by that in New York and Calcutta. But the background of war and destruction in Naples lends special character and urgency.

The first time I saw the Casa Mia neighborhood, a few years after the war, the return from the caves had just gotten underway. The most temporary kinds of shelters had been thrown together with scrap lumber and tar paper, and I remember reading on some of the exposed boards of some of the shacks, information about New York manufacturing concerns. Some said *Kelloggs Cornflakes*. Some said *Beware! Explosives!*

From its beginning Casa Mia worked closely with the older Casa Materna which provided some permanent care for orphaned children and temporary care for those whose parents were getting established in the city. Casa Mia was liaison and referral between people and social resources of government, school, private charities, jobs. Hot lunch and club programs were organized. Individual and family counseling were provided. Social workers came from America and England to assist in the work, which was supported almost entirely by the church now known as The United Church of Christ in the United States.

My later visits saw new developments in the neighborhood, with all the caves emptied, and even some of the temporary shelters done away with, in favor of beginnings of housing projects in various parts of the city. Every time a family could move into a permanent dwelling, the vacated tar paper structure was destroyed. Casa Mia was in the business of helping people to move out. One great temporary shelter, a stone barracks called Bianchini remained in use, and several thousand people still lived there.

On my last visit recently I might never have known this neighborhood, except for the familiar little two-story building with its big sign *CASA MIA*. Almost everything else looked strange. Even vast Bianchini was different. Although it was still there, it had been entirely evacuated, and the great stone doorways were sealed with cement.

Riding on the trolley out of Portici and into Naples I noticed that the temporary shelters were all gone. Some rubble was left, and there was a good deal of empty space left where buildings had been torn down. A few small businesses had sprung up, stores of various kinds, small eating places. But I looked at what appeared to be a business section of Naples. Among the buildings was Casa Mia, just off the streetcar line, flanked by small stores. In front of Casa Mia and behind it, were empty spaces where there had been a small city of refugee shacks.

Most of the people had gone to housing projects in various parts of the city but Naples could not build housing fast enough to meet the demand. A large number had clustered together and settled in a neighborhood they created for themselves. Dr. Tiofilo prepared to serve the increasing numbers of people crowding into alley ways and courtyards off the business streets by building a hospital to help meet their health care needs.

Casa Mia's little headquarters building is a beehive of activity—as it was six or ten or fifteen years ago. Its full program includes housing, of course, but it also provides help for young boys who are able to go on to trade schools in the city.

The first of these two stories from Casa Mia is about Georgio who lives there, and formerly lived at Casa Materna. The story came from Dr. Tiofilo.

Dr. Tiofilo was able to escape from his patients and have dinner with the family only two or three times a week, and his late arrival was always a joyous occasion. I grew accustomed to the electricity in the air, to the special feeling of celebration, to the way the little girls at the next table sprang from their chairs and sped to the kitchen to fetch the doctor's soup and his cheese and his bread and anything else that was required. Suddenly the room had a brilliant new center. The doctor was dining with us.

On a particular evening, which I remember as the "Georgio" evening, Dr. Tiofilo was clearly jubilant and highly amused about something. We were laughing even before he told us. In fact everybody knew that something wonderfully funny was about to happen when he pulled out the empty chair which was always kept ready for him and sat down in it jauntily, pulled up close to the table and reached for a paper napkin. He turned to kiss his pretty wife as he unfolded the napkin, doing both with a flourish. Olivia tried to look severe, but we knew she didn't feel that way.

"So, I have no need to worry about my old age!" he announced to any and all that would hear. "I have an assurance!"

"You are not so old!" Olivia told him. "You only work too much."

"I am an old man!" he insisted, as if she had not spoken. "You have an old man for a husband, but we shall all be cared for, never fear."

"Who will take care of us, then?" she demanded, still pretending to be severe.

"Who?" He sat up straight and tall, held up the knife in one hand, the fork in the other, and looked warmly around the table. "Who? But it is Georrrrrrrgio. Of course!" Dr. Tiofilo spoke like a Roman, not the Neopolitan that he was, with the r's rolling out one after another like a wave thundering up the beach. Olivia stopped pretending and laughed good-naturedly.

"Georgio, indeed!" she exclaimed. "He needs someone to take care of *him*! But look at him now!"

And then I saw Georgio, for I knew it must be Georgio. He had come through the door behind the doctor, and now he stood by the table, blushing. He might have heard what they had said, but I thought not.

"Welcome!" Dr. Tiofilo shouted to him. "Today you are my guest. Tomorrow, remember, I am your guest!" He reached up to grasp the boy's hand and shook it firmly. "My benefactor!" he shouted, and everybody laughed.

Georgio laughed and blushed and replied to Dr. Tiofilo with a sweeping bow, almost to his knees, so that everybody laughed again. It was easy to see that Georgio was at home in Casa Materna, although he lived at Casa Mia and did not intend to have dinner with us.

"He goes to his school now," Pastor Emanuele said aside to me. "He is a night student at the engineering school in Naples."

"Well, then, if you do not stay for dinner with us, let me tell you that I have a present for you, Georgio," Dr. Tiofilo went on. "Tomorrow I will bring it to Casa Mia. It is a pretty ribbon for you to tie your curls."

Georgio laughed again and patted his hair, which was long, in the fashion then, and curled. He replied in Italian, and there was laughter. Then he went out through the door, saluting Dr. Tiofilo as he left us.

"He is about to have a good job, that one!" the doctor said to me after Georgio had gone and while one of the girls was bringing more soup for him. "With Fiat in Rome. But first he must establish citizenship in Naples. And that is likely to take the rest of his lifetime!"

36

He made the Italian gesture that means everything—futility, boredom, exasperation, surrender.

I remarked that Georgio was a fine figure of a young man. He was not just handsome. He was a Greek god. Blond, chiseled features, tall but not too tall, muscular but not too much, broad shoulders but not out of proportion. He was perfect, and apparently unaware of it. The hair was long to save trouble, I guessed. It had nothing to do with vanity or the mode. Georgio looked as though he couldn't care less about what anybody in the world might think of his looks.

"He is about to have a good job, that one!" the doctor repeated. "It is what he is trained to do."

"But the papers—" I began.

"Papers, papers," he exclaimed. "The boy was born at Reti, and that is the trouble." Reti, I knew, was a border town.

"Of course I can see that he isn't Italian," I said.

"True. But it matters even more that he is not Neopolitan born," Dr. Tiofilo said. "Hungarian but born in Naples would be all right. He must get the documents from Reti saying who were his parents, and if they were indeed citizens of Reti. Who knows? And how little it matters, when he can do the job! And by the time we learn all these irrelevant things about him, if indeed they can be learned at all, there is again the question of who is his father. And then there are more months to wait. And perhaps the job is gone long before."

The rest of the people at the table agreed, and it sounded familiar to me, too. Red tape must be universal, I thought.

"But Georgio has the solution!" Dr. Tiuofilo exclaimed, laughing again. "He has solved the problem." He paused. "Do you know the paper that asks for 'name of place of residence, name of parent, name of father's job'?"

We all knew.

Dr. Tiofilo chuckled delightedly.

"Georgio writes this way," he said. "Name, *Santi*. Residence, *Casa Materna*. Occupation, *Doctor*!"

Olivia laughed with the others, but was concerned, too.

"What did you say to him then?" she asked. "Did you explain that it is not so easy to claim you for a parent?"

37

He shook his head.

"I said," he told us, "I said, 'Well, if I am the parent, then of course I shall hope that you will get this job and make a good deal of money and take care of me, since I shall soon be an old man. You will be the *bastone delle sua vecciaia*—the staff of my old age—'"

"The staff of your old age, indeed!" Olivia said. "What did he respond to that? Did he want to take the responsibility?"

"He was delighted!" the doctor assured her. "He said that no one, not you, dear Livy, not anyone here is to have one small worry, and I myself am not to worry. He, Georrrrrrgio will take care of Dr. Santi and all of Dr. Santi's family, and for all of Casa Materna, when he is rich!"

"Well, you would do well to collect from your patients in the meantime!" she warned him.

But I could see that she was touched, and so were we all. After the fun the doctor was suddenly, dramatically, serious.

"Georgio is especially my son," he assured me. "He is a sacred charge. I have this boy as a gift from his mother, when she died. It happens often, in this place. But Georgio is a gift to me."

Some interruption happened then to leave the story to be continued from there. Perhaps the children came to be hugged and to say good night. But we spoke no more of Georgio that evening.

My next meeting with Georgio was at Casa Mia, where he lived and worked while attending the night school. Dr. Tiofilo took me in the Fiat, and I was pleased to find that most of the way was becoming familiar. Casa Mia was the same small, square, two-story building, and we stopped as we had long ago, to ring the bell before the great iron door swung open for us. It stayed locked except when somebody came and pounded on it or rang the bell. Then a head would appear in the window overhead to look over the visitor before deciding whether to open the gate. When that had happened, we were admitted, Fiat and all, to the cobblestone floor of the patio just beyond the gate. This was Casa Mia.

Georgio appeared a little later, with his hair cut short, which delighted Dr. Tiofilo. His companion, an English boy named Robert, had curls enough for both of them.

It now appeared that my day was to be an escorted tour through the Casa Mia neighborhood, and then into the business parts of Naples. My escorts would be Georgio, who, according to Dr. Tiofilo, spoke English "excellently," and Robert, who would interpret if necessary.

The tour is not a part of Georgio's story, except that it did give me a chance to observe him rather closely, as well as to look at the streets and small courtyards we journeyed through. Georgio's excellent English I had no opportunity to admire, because he refused to use it and spoke only Italian. Robert was a good interpreter, however, and we all seemed to speak the same language when tea time came. I treated gratefully with ice cream, which seems to be universally understood. It was pleasant to be the object of devoted attention of two of the most attractive young men in Naples, as I thought.

I was returned to Casa Materna, not Casa Mia, and by trolley, not on foot, for my escorts were worn out. We found Dr. Tiofilo in the garden, sitting on a bench, enjoying a rare moment of leisure. He looked a little uneasy on a garden seat, I thought.

"Well, well!" he greeted us, as if we had come from a long trip. "You have seen Naples?"

We had, indeed, and had calluses to prove it. He led us to a stone bench down by the garden fountain and dismissed the boys.

"What do you think of Georgio?" he asked me at once. "Did he talk to you."

"He talked," I said, "in Italian. But I understood a little of it and Robert interpreted some. I like 'the stick of your old age.'"

"Well, he is as dear to me as one of my own," Dr. Tiofilo said, seriously. "Indeed he is my own, the gift of his mother when she died. He is Hungarian, as you could see, born in Reti, in the north."

"It's clear he isn't Italian," I agreed.

"His mother was Hungarian," the doctor said. "His father is unknown. We think he may have been a good man and believe Georgio is like him."

It was not an unusual story, and there is at least one other in this group of stories, which tells of a child born out of wedlock, and in a refugee camp. Georgio's mother may have been a widow, or unmarried, when she came with him from Reti to the vicinity of one of

39

the refugee camps Dr. Tifilo organized after the war. She lived with the small boy outside the camp, because "followers" were not admitted. The man who was with her at that time was a Hungarian sailor who shipped off suddenly one morning. He was never heard from again. A few months later she was the mother of twins.

"This is when we found her," Dr. Tiofilo told me. He was serious now, and sad, and very different from the doctor joking at the table.

"It is sad that so many children come where there are already too many," he said. "And yet every child is a gift from God, and we do not say that he has no right to live. Perhaps there was a special purpose in the birth of these two at this time, for the mother indeed seemed to change. She was a good woman from that time, and even was invited to bring her babies and the little boy, to live in the camp."

"How did Georgio happen to come to Casa Materna?" I asked. But I could see that my question reflected how my thoughts were jumping about.

"She became ill," he said. "It was tuberculosis. And after the twins were a little bigger she went to the hospital."

"With two small babies, and a little boy!" I exclaimed.

Dr. Tiofilo nodded.

"You can have no idea what a refugee camp is like," he told me. "Even young as they were there was a danger of harm from the men to the little girl."

"And of course Georgio was too small to care for them," I added.

"Of course, much too small, although he tried." Dr. Tiofilo smiled as he remembered. "Georgio was always one to care for others, young and old!"

We both remembered "the stick of his old age."

"Well, I said to her that I would take the babies to Casa Materna until she would recover. We could not keep them very long, I said, because we had no facilities for very young children. And there was not even room here for Georgio. But I tried to be reassuring, because this was her worry. I tried to comfort the poor woman."

A few days after that, and while the children were spending their "short time" at Casa Materna, the doctor was called to the hospital.

"If ever I have seen fear in a woman's eyes it was in the eyes of this one," Dr. Tiofilo said. "She was beautiful, as I remember, and she was terrified."

"She looked like Georgio, maybe?"

He tried to remember.

"Not so much, I believe. She was dark." Then he smiled. "She had curls, I think, like Georgio's before he cut them off! He was afraid I would tie them with ribbons maybe."

"Was she afraid of the operation?" I asked.

"She was convinced she would die," he answered, becoming serious again. "When she talked to me she said, 'I must have the operation in two days, and that will be my last time in this world.'

"I tried to reassure her. I explained that most people recover, and that she might be strong soon again. 'The operation is to cure, not to kill,' I told her. But she would not believe.

"'Dr. Santi,' she told me, 'I shall die. I shall never live from that operation. And it is all right to die, but I want to be sure my children will be cared for. I want you to take my son, my Georgio, and those two little ones. Take them for your own. Especially I want you to make Georgio into a good man, because his father was good.'"

Tears came into his eyes, as he remembered.

"What was I to do then?" he asked. "I told her again that she would live. I told her she would recover and live many years with her children.

"'Dr. Santi,' she said to me, 'Since I was a young girl I have never known anyone in the world who could be trusted. Only Casa Materna. And maybe I am wrong about Casa Materna, too. Maybe you are like all the others. Maybe you will deceive me, too!'

"Casa Materna will not deceive you," I told her. "She smiled and it was beautiful, I tell you!"

"'Take my babies, then,' she said. 'And take my Georgio. His father was a good man. He is a good boy. He tries to be kind. Help him to grow in wisdom and goodness. He has not had much chance.'

41

"Well, I told her again that she would have good care, and would surely recover, but she seemed not even to hear. She only said again that she would die happy knowing that her children were cared for, and that her Georgio would grow to be a good man."

He paused for a moment before continuing.

"I think perhaps she was determined to die, that woman!" he said then. "The operation was not a serious one. I was right in reassuring her. But even if she lived, what might have become of the children? I believe she thought that if she died they could come to Casa Materna." He shook his head sadly.

"Well, we cannot fathom the reasons. No more can we fail to obey a dying request. She did not survive the operation. She was already dead when it was over. And it was a pity, for she was not an old woman. Her children would have had their chance, if she had lived."

"Georgio is a handsome boy," I observed. "He is really beautiful."

"And good. He is a good boy. And he has a good mind."

Casa Materna then became parent to the three Hungarian children. The twins were pretty children, and of average ability, Dr. Tiofilo thought. But Georgio was superior. His father must have been an intelligent man, and attractive.

"One wonders about these things," he said. "Only God knows. But I believe Georgio carries the best of blood in his veins."

He was by far the best of the students in the school at Casa Materna, which was the best school in Naples. He passed the standard examinations with high honors and earned a scholarship to the engineering school in Naples, where he would graduate first, in a short time.

"They recognized his ability there, from the beginning," Dr. Tiofilo recalled. "Georgio was so outstanding that the director of the school offered to adopt him in place of his own son who was a wastrel! Can you imagine it?"

I could not, but Dr. Tiofilo said it happened often in Italy. A man without children, or with a son who had disappointed him, would adopt another, to carry his name.

"He wanted to educate Georgio in another profession," he said. "The director of the engineering college wanted to prepare Georgio for the priesthood."

I was intrigued.

"That speaks well for Casa Materna!" I said. "You reared him for being a priest, maybe! But what did Georgio say?"

Dr. Tiofilo laughed delightedly.

"Georgio said he was a Protestant, not a Catholic, and therefore could not possibly become a priest. And the director was disappointed. But he said that if the Protestants had anything in their religion that was something like a priest, he hoped Georgio would be one. He might be a Protestant priest, the director suggested."

"Did Georgio like the idea?" I asked.

"He liked it," said the doctor. "But he liked it in his own way. He told the director that Protestants can be priests whatever they are doing to make a living. 'Sir Director,' he said to that man, 'as a Protestant I can be an electrician and a priest at the same time!'"

At that moment I realized that we were not alone. In that quick cat-like way he had, Georgio had appeared out of nowhere, and I thought he must know he was the subject of our conversation. Especially he would know if he understood English "excellently" as Dr. Tiofilo had said. But he did not appear to be self-conscious at all.

Dr. Tiofilo stood up and clapped him on the shoulder. But had to reach up, because Georgio was the taller.

"Well, where are the curls?" he asked, and Georgio blushed but did not answer. "So here is 'the stick of my old age!' Yes, and I think he will succeed!"

It was the last time I was to see Georgio.

4. Lili of Bianchini

Bianchini is a mammoth stone barracks and stable that began as a king's palace. During World War II Bianchini housed some of Mussolini's cavalry troops and their horses, and after the war was home for over a thousand refugees. The monster lodging place was condemned and then emptied by official edict. Some families were moved to other quarters in the neighborhood, some to new government housing projects, and others simply disappeared, melting quietly into the city's maelstrom.

Years ago when I first saw Bianchini it was full of people who lived there but hardly went so far as to call it home. One would not call a dungeon home, or a stable, or a place where maybe a hundred people share one latrine, and a family of six or so live in one small enclosure. But they lived, somehow, and I met a friend there whom I have never forgotten. In fact my journey back this time was partly a pilgrimage to look for a woman named Kate and her baby girl, Lili, who must be a big girl now, or a young lady.

I strolled about the streets surrounding the old barracks, so big it covered what would be a large sized city block in New York, and marveled at the speed with which nature can cover up man's works. I knew that the last great doorway had been sealed with stone only a year before, and now the ruined walls were already covered with green moss. I marveled, too, at the lonesomeness of it, and how this place was deserted and silent and yet crying from life that had lately crowded within its walls.

The woman I was looking for had been the housekeeper at Casa Mia years before. The workers there had called her Kate, which obviously was not her real name, but she like it, as she liked everything American. Lili, the baby, was the blonde child of this Italian mother and an unknown American soldier, she told me, and they lived in a room of Bianchini with three other children, each one born of a different father, each father, like Lili's, unknown.

So, on this return mission, everywhere in the area of Casa Mia, I asked people I met who might understand a little English, "Do you remember a woman called Kate? Do you know where she would be now?"

Some remembered her vaguely, or thought so. She was a colorful person, the kind one would remember, Southern Italian, dark and intense. But no one could tell me exactly when Kate had left Bianchini, or exactly where she might have gone. Perhaps she had left long before the official closing, perhaps with the great crowd that stayed on to the end, until they were forced to leave. She had not been housekeeper at Casa Mia for a long time.

Perhaps Kate and her children were still living somewhere in those crowded small streets that honeycomb the area fanning off the main artery passing Bianchini. It is very easy to be lost among streets hardly wide enough for two people to walk abreast, and so jam packed with living, too. My friend Kate and her babies might be living in any of these streets, or the crowded courtyards opening off them. I might run across them any time, or I might not, people told me.

"Will you know her?" they asked. "Would you remember how she looks?"

I thought I would remember Kate. Even among the crowded two million people in the New Naples I would know her.

Of course, they said, she might have gone to one of the new housing projects. I thought that a flat in a housing project would be a decided improvement over one room in Bianchini.

But they would shake their heads doubtfully. It might be an improvement. But it might not be, too. So many people pouring into these new structures are from so many kinds of places. They came from Bianchini, of course, and also from the caves outside the city, and from the refugee camps. And they were not all Italians, either. Some were Yugoslavian, some Hungarian, or whatever. And there was no one to help them learn how to live in the new quarters, all just alike. And there was no money at all, to get settled with. Life could be hard in a housing project.

Kate had made a stable in Bianchini look like a home for herself, three small children and a baby. I thought she could handle a place in a housing project all right.

So we talked this way, and no one was very hopeful that in the New Naples I would ever find a trace of Kate and Lili. But the more I talked with people, the more I was convinced that I knew about Lili of Bianchini.

I asked many questions.

"It would be likely, wouldn't it, that Lili would have done *this*? Or thought *that*? Or learned something else? And wouldn't she have felt *this* way, probably? Or *that* way? How would she have grown? What would she have known? What experiences would have surrounded her growing up? Would it be *this* way, then?"

The answers, with many suggestions, would always come— serious, somewhat skeptical, but always sympathetic and half-assenting. "Yes, of course it could be that way. One cannot say surely, but it could have happened so. It is possible! It is possible!"

So Lili's story is made with the help of many interested people, and some of them at Casa Materna and Casa Mia encourage me, saying that it is very likely that it all did take place for Lili, just this way!

There were two places Lili remembered from the time she was born. One was Bianchini where she lived. The other was Casa Mia where her mother worked a while back.

The white room in the big building she knew at Bianchini, her mother called a "stall." It was whitewashed with the cheapest kind of lime, but Lili only knew that it was shining clean, different from any of the other rooms. They were gray and dirty and smelled of the latrine down the corridor. Lili's room in Bianchini kept smelling sweet with lime.

Lili remembered that it was a long way to the top of that room. It was so far up that as a baby she always got interested in looking at other things before her eyes could travel to the ceiling.

She knew that her mother called the room a "stall" and the big building a "stable" but since Lili had never seen either one, the names meant very little to her. There was not much furniture. In one corner was an altar with a crucifix and a beautiful picture of the Virgin. They all five had to kneel there and say the prayer morning and night. Kate

46

whipped them if they missed. And they all five—Lili and her mother and the others—slept on the same bed until Giovanni ran away. They never saw him again. Her mother exclaimed, "Scugnizzo!" which was as good as to say, "You juvenile delinquent! You gang member!" or "Good riddance to bad rubbish," and that was that.

Giovanni was dark with the blackest eyes. Lili barely remembered him, but she knew that her mother called him black and said his father was a black Sicilian. Lili secretly thought her mother was just as black as Giovanni. Rosaria, the second of the three, was dark, too, but not quite so dark as Giovanni. Rosaria's father, Lili understood, was a Yugoslavian. Petro was the next one to Lili and his father was Neapolitan, but his mother either didn't know much about him or preferred not to talk about him. She seemed not to feel much responsibility herself for those three, or for their existence, even. She gave them food when she could get it and even deprived herself so they could eat. She commanded them to pray.

But the one child she really loved was Lili and Lili knew it. From the day she was born she knew herself to be the favorite. The father of this one Kate proudly referred to as "the American. She would hold the baby up before the cracked mirror and point to Lili's blue eyes and flaxen curls.

"Americano!" she cried ecstatically.

For Kate and for Lili, too, because she early learned it that way, America was a beautiful land full of handsome, blue-eyed, blonde people, all rich, all generous, all happy. America and heaven confused themselves in Lili's young mind.

"Much money!" Kate would say. She knew a few English words and commanded Lili to learn all of them. "Money" was a favorite. "Hi, ya, babe!" delighted her. "OK" was her cheerful response to everything. "Cheerio, pip pip," which she pronounced "peep peep" was her gay farewell. "Kate" was the name she liked to be called, and if she had another one Lili never learned it.

Lili learned all these words, and knew that hearing them made her mother happy. And because Kate so extravagantly worshipped the blonde baby, Lili responded with the same kind of single-minded devotion to her mother. It occurred to her to wonder about her

47

American father, but she never asked. Instinctively she knew it would not be a useful question. Later on she began of her own accord to think of him as dead.

Kate often carried the baby in her arms, long after Lili was much too large to be carried, and she always took her to work with her. Kate loved her work, partly because any kind of job was good luck in those days, and partly because there were some beautiful Americans connected with it. She was not the best housekeeper in the world, but she brought her special variety of zest to the life of Casa Mia. The neighborhood house was more home to Kate and Lili than the white-washed stall in Bianchini.

Held tightly in her mother's arms, or beside her and clinging to her hand, Lili listened at the doorway of the singing room, where the Casa Mia children sometimes gathered in groups during the day. She listened to the same tunes again when her mother hummed and whistled them as she scrubbed the floors or dusted the furniture. It seemed to Lili that she must have begun her life with the sound of Casa Mia music in her head.

And so it was that those two places, Bianchini and Casa Mia, but Casa Mia more than Bianchini, became the baby Lili's frame of reference and she grew to be a girl of three or four, safe in her mother's affection, not very much aware of anyone, or any place else.

After Giovanni disappeared there was more room, and they soon forgot about him. Then one day Rosaria, although much too young as her mother casually remarked, got married and went to live in another room of Bianchini with her man. They saw very little of Rosaria after that. And then Petro got arrested and put in jail for stealing, and by the time Lili was twelve they were alone, she and her mother, in the white stall, praying together. Kate guarded Lili fiercely, as if she were a precious jewel.

Lili was pretty. She could see it for herself in the cracked looking glass, and she could see it in the dark inviting eyes of men and big boys who watched whenever Kate and Lili came out of their room together. For Kate seldom allowed Lili to be alone in the corridors of Bianchini, not even to go to the toilet, which was quite a long walk from the stall. Doggedly, Kate accompanied her, and Lili was glad to be safe from the watching eyes of men who stood aimlessly in the dark hallway and in the great front doorway, and around the doorway on the outside of the barracks. They looked, they invited, but they never spoke. They did not dare.

With her brother Petro before he went to jail, it was different. He had learned all the ways of the city, outside Bianchini and Casa Mia, and before he was arrested and taken off to jail, Lili learned many things from him. She learned about picking pockets on the streets for one thing, and because Lili was different and so beautiful, people looked at her face, so that her nimble fingers were free. One or two times, when she and Petro were free, she did a good business and brought money home to her mother.

Kate was of two minds about the new occupation of Lili. The money was acceptable. Nor had Kate any scruples about stealing wallets of the rich. It was a way of borrowing from the people who had, for the help of the people who had not. Her reasoning was uncomplicated. People who needed something ought to have it. People who had it ought to provide. The only problem, for Kate, was whether or not stealing was safe for Lili.

As for Lili, of course, she saw the job simply as a way of helping her mother to get along, and she had also some satisfaction in performing skillfully. That there was a kind of shadow over the profession, she was aware.

"It is true that they would not do this at Casa Mia," Lili told her mother, as they puzzled it over.

"And you would not do it at Casa Mia, either," Kate agreed. "It is very simple. You do one thing at Casa Mia. You do another thing in the streets. It is very simple. I only fear that you may be caught and arrested."

Neither of them was quite satisfied with the explanation, reasonable as it sounded, and neither knew exactly why it was not quite right. But after Petro was arrested and sent to jail, Kate forbade any further pocket picking. Lili was disappointed because she had become adept at the trade. And she was glad, too, because after she stopped stealing she felt a little better about going to Casa Mia and singing with the other children.

Summer was wonderful because as soon as it was warm enough the Casa Mia children made journeys by bus to the beach for swimming, and during those summer visits Lili learned to know the beautiful Casa Materna, the palace on the edge of Naples Bay. At Casa Materna the children lived all around the clock. The Casa Mia children were only visitors and had to go home in the late afternoon.,

Kate went along with Lili for a few times before she agreed to let the little girl go without her. But with or without Kate, every morning Lili, with the Casa Mia children, climbed in the big bus and rode away to Casa Materna. They came there early for morning prayers outside the great, red palace. Facing the fountain and the gardens, green and bright with oleander and bougainvillea, they sang songs of praise and thanksgiving, the same songs Lili had learned at Casa Mia.

Often Lili forgot to sing, as she looked at the loveliness about her. She had seen pictures of Paradise, which looked like the garden at Casa Materna. Heaven, Casa Materna and America—now all seemed alike to her.

After the "worship," as they called it, all of the children raced down to the beach, threw off their dresses and raced over the hot black sand in the swim suits that they had worn under their street clothing. Lili liked paddling in the shallow warm dark water close to the beach, and she liked digging holes in the black sand and watching the dark water rise up as if they were little wells. Sometimes she liked drying off in the sunshine, and shaking the sand off her warm brown legs before she put on her dress.

But other times, long before the man in charge blew the whistle that called them all to the bus, Lili would slip away from the others, run behind the dressing shelter, put on her dress over her wet swim suit, and then steal all alone up the steps to the palace and garden. There she would walk quietly about. Or she would choose one spot to sit by herself. Usually it was close to the fountain, and near the century cactus. She had heard that the cactus would bloom one time after a hundred years and then would die.

"It would be exciting if the big tree would bloom one day for me!" she said to herself. "But it would be sad for it to die!"

Often she would hear the buzz of the saw in the boys' shop on the other side of the gardens. Sometimes there would be singing from here and there about the gardens. Always in the background on those warm sunny mornings she could hear the children shouting down on the beach. It all looked and sounded and felt like heaven or America.

Lili wondered what it would be like to live in the palace and be a Casa Materna child. Once in a while, when she was alone and no one could hear, she said out loud, "I would like to come and stay here, and it would be my home." But then she felt guilty and sad, because there was Kate in Bianchini. Lili needed Kate, but since she was born she had known that Kate needed Lili even more. She knew, and it was understood that she would always be a visitor here in heaven, and that she would always go home to Bianchini when the whistle blew.

But she kept being curious to know what happened to Casa Materna children. She asked some of the ones who rode the bus with her from Casa Mia about that. They thought perhaps Casa Materna children were much like other children.

She asked her mother, but Kate did not know.

"Would you like to go and live at Casa Materna?" she asked Lili.

Lili quickly said that she would not, not at all.

One time, down on the beach, she had a long talk with a boy named Georgio, who lived at Casa Materna.

"Does it make you different if you sleep here?" she asked. "Would it make me change, if I stayed here after the bus leaves?"

Georgio was not sure, but he thought perhaps it would make a good deal of difference.

"We are a family here," he said. "Everybody is kind and loves everybody else."

"How can you love everybody?" Lili asked curiously. "How does it feel?"

"It feels like you are all together," he said. "And you aren't afraid of anything."

Lili was puzzled, but then so was Georgio.

"It is something you know, but you can't say it," he said finally. "You *want* to do things!"

51

"What things?" Lili asked. Georgio hardly knew. "I want to do things, too," Lili said. "I am good at stealing, and I used to give the money to my mother, and she was glad to get it. I stole a thousand lira from a fat man on the street, and he never knew it at all. And I felt good because it was helping my mother."

"Maybe you felt good to help your mother," Georgio said, cautiously. "But what happened to the fat man?"

Lili didn't know. But he was no concern of hers. She had never seen him again.

"My mother made me stop stealing," she said then. "After my brother Petro was taken to jail she made me stop."

"Pastor Santi says God owns everything," Georgio said. "He says you can't steal anything from anybody because it isn't anybody's—it is all God's."

"I pray to God every morning and night," Lili said. "And to the Virgin. My mother makes me."

"Your mother is good, then," Georgio acknowledged. "Pastor Santi prays every morning and night, too."

"My mother is good!" Lili repeated fervently. "My mother is good!"

It seemed a short time that day before the whistle blew!

Lili didn't notice, but Kate did, when the men came to look over the great Bianchini. They were well dressed and officers, everyone said. Right away the word began going around that something would happen to Bianchini. Everybody wondered, but nobody knew anything to do except to wait. Kate said that was the way with poor people. They always had to wait.

And then the next thing they knew there were placards on the place announcing that everyone must leave, as quickly as possible.

Kate went, with some of the others, to hunt for places where she and Lili might live. They had meetings at Bianchini to talk things over. Some of them wanted to go on a strike and refuse to leave Bianchini. Some told about the housing projects, brand new buildings that the government was building for people who had no homes. A family might have three small rooms instead of one. And every section had its own bathroom. Kate went to see them and thought they were

52

beautiful. They had windows. Of course they were a long way from Casa Mia and Bianchini.

"There will be no Bianchini any more," she told Lili. "And it will be hard to leave Casa Mia. It is a good job."

"I must work, then," Lili said. "I must steal again. And I will bring the money to you."

"You are getting too big to steal now," Kate reminded her. "You must be small and spry, to keep from being caught."

One day, when Lili came back with the bus to Casa Mia, she did not find her mother there as usual, and for the first time she made her way alone to Bianchini. It seemed like a long and lonely walk through the streets, but she knew the way. For the first time she walked through the door at Bianchini alone, and up the steps and along the dark corridor to her own room, avoiding, as Kate had taught her to do, the curious and inviting looks of the men who stood in the shadows. Some of them called to her, but she did not answer.

When she reached her own room she saw that the door was ajar, and instinctively stopped before going in. She could hear voices, and she knew it was one of the men who came to see Kate sometimes. Lili might have gone on in, but she had a feeling Kate might not like her to go in. She waited, listening, just outside. No one had told her that it is wrong to listen.

"But why do you want to stay in Bianchini?" the man was asking. "It is cold. There are too many people. It smells. It is bad for your health here. And there, in the place I have found for you, you have two rooms, and windows to look out of. You will like it there."

"I earn money here," Kate reminded him. "I am a housekeeper."

"It's a poor way to earn money," he said. "You know easier ones, that make more money. Much more money."

"Not so much now as it used to be," Kate said wearily. "I am getting too old."

"Well—" he hesitated. "You are not so young or so beautiful, that is true. But Lili is beautiful."

"Diavolo!" she screamed. "Get out, pig that you are." She made the noise of spitting. "You are not fit to speak her name!"

53

The man laughed. He did not seem angry at all.

"But it's a good life!" he protested. "You ought to know."

Kate was silent. Then she said, "She is too young."

"Nobody is too young," he reminded her. "It is possible to be too old, but nobody is ever too young." When she was silent he continued. "Beauty is a talent, and Lili has it. You can teach her how to use it."

"She will be cheated!"

"Not if you teach her well," he said. "It is a trade to be learned, and you can teach her. You know how."

"Diavolo!" Kate exclaimed again. "You are a pig!"

But she did not sound as angry as the words seemed. She sounded tired.

"Let me help you," he said. "Call on me any time."

He went out of the room without seeing Lili behind the big door.

Lili waited quietly until he had gone down the corridor and into the latrine at the end, before she went into the room. There Kate was sitting on the one chair, studying the crucifix on the altar. She stood up quickly and began picking the wax flowers off the altar.

"They are old," she remarked without saying, "Hello," or explaining why she had not been at Casa Mia to walk home with Lili. "We must have new flowers for the altar."

Lili told her about the day at Casa Materna, and about her talk with Georgio. Kate did not appear to pay much attention, but when Lili finished she said suddenly, "Would you like to go and live at Casa Materna?"

Lili said again that she would not.

"Did you find a new place for us to live?" she asked her mother.

"It is too far," Kate said. "I could not work at Casa Mia."

"I could work," Lili said. "I can steal again, and get a good deal of money. I am still small enough."

"You might get into jail," Kate said.

"I am too skillful," Lili insisted. "I am very good."

"You are too old for stealing," Kate said then. "Only children are good, and you are twelve."

"I am beautiful," Lili said. "And I am old enough, too, for the trade." Kate knew what she meant.

"You don't know about it," Kate said.

"I can learn," Lili insisted. "It is a good job."

"It is a good job," Kate admitted. "Mostly it is plenty of money and plenty easy. But—"

Lili did not answer, and Kate looked at her quickly.

"You are too young," she said then. "We will find another way."

But Lili was not troubled about the "trade." She was quiet because she was remembering again some of the things Georgio had said at Casa Materna, and suddenly she realized that she was hearing in her mind the words of the worship service they had had in front of the red palace before they had gone to swim.

They stood in line under the words, "Suffer the children to come to me."

She heard Pastor Santi's words very clearly now, and this was strange because she did not hear them at all in the morning! But now they came to her very clearly, as though she were back before the palace.

"God is the owner of everything that is. He made it and he owns it—everything. God made you and me. He made our bodies and our minds, and all of these are his. He lets us use them, for him.

"He will never forsake us, no, not even in the midst of the crowds of enemies and the noise of battle.

"God is love, and all that love love God, and God is the loving Lord of all.

"Fear not! Only love. For God is love!"

Then Lili realized that her mother was looking at her anxiously, waiting for her to speak, to say something. She felt very good and very strong.

"You are good, Mama!" she said softly. "I love you. We are both good. We will find the way together."

5. The Happy Story of Elisabetta
(Fabio Santi's Story)

Fabio Santi was mayor of Portici when he died. He was the only Protestant mayor ever to be elected in that Roman Catholic city, and Via Fabio Santi will stay to memorialize the most progressive administration this community has known. Beyond Naples and Portici the courts of Italy will always recall a famous case which Pastor Santi's lawyer son argued and won against Mussolini himself. That was the time when Il Duce tried to close Casa Materna.

But Fabio Santi himself would most treasure a different kind of memorial, and he has that too, in the many young men and women whose lives are different and better because of him. Some are alive today because of him, and there is a special one of these, a young girl who lives now in New York. The story is Elisabetta's, and it is Fabio's, but it happened like this.

There came a bright morning, a few days after my arrival at Casa Materna, when the bay was blue and gold, with a splendid look across to the islands, and sideways off to that enigmatic old Vesuvius, who watched over us intrepidly.

I had strolled down from breakfast, to sit with my pencil and pad on one of the lower steps of the terrace. It was easy to be transported back two hundred years to the days when royalty would have been here on the terrace instead of me. Easy, that is, except for the steady background of children's voices, not like sleepy chickens now, but shrill and sweet and wide awake, on the terrace, on the balconies above, and all through the gardens. I kept making pencil scratches in my notebook pretending to be hard at work, and all the while wishing only to look and look and look at the sea picture spread out in front of me.

Then would you believe a surprise hug and a moist kiss on my cheek, and I turned fast enough to catch, but only with an eye, the smallest boy, who had tip-toed down the steps behind me. The kiss, a stiff little bow, a magic smile that made all the Bay of Naples sparkle more, and baby Andrea was back up the steps and off to charm somebody else. But in the excitement I became aware of a good deal of activity going on in the office at the top of the steps.

The long room up there opens all the way across the broad terrace, with wide triple doors, and I fancy it may once have been a gathering place for royal bathers when they strolled up dripping from the beach for a chat after swimming, perhaps for a cup of Italian coffee, or something else. Today it is a formal office, speaking eloquently of Fabio Santi, the lawyer, who was director here when he died. Giant book cases go all the way up to a twenty-foot ceiling and are filled with his law library, including the very books that helped him carry the famous eviction case to Rome.

As I climbed the steps and opened the big door into his office, I thought of Fabio, great in heart and voice and stature, but especially to be remembered for his gentleness with little children. I remembered how they came to him all day long, one and two at a time, on tip-toe across the patterned tile floor and right up to the big desk where two telephones were always ringing. However busy he was, and Fabio was always busy, he had time for making every single child, as that child came to him, the most important person in the world, at that particular moment.

On this morning the telephones were ringing as usual, and it was all that Teofilo and Emanuele and two secretaries, one Italian and one American, could do together to keep everything answered. Emanuele was dictating in English between phone calls and asides to his brother, mostly in a flood of Italian. I was surprised and pleased when he remembered to change to English to say, "Good morning!" to me.

"Apparently you are not so efficient as your ancestor," I remarked, taking the chair he indicated. "Julius Caesar could dictate to seven secretaries all at the same time."

"Julius Caesar had no telephone," Emanuele answered quickly.

And then by some kind of cheerful Casa Materna magic we were suddenly relaxed and leisurely. The two secretaries disappeared with their shorthand tablets, the phones seemed to understand they were not to ring for a while, and Emanuele and Tiofilo were ready to think of stories about children, and of course about Fabio, for they always liked to include him in our conversations. I suggested that we include a story from Fabio in this collection, even if it should have to be about a child no longer at Casa Materna.

"I hate to leave here without a Fabio story," I said.

Emanuele looked up, as all of us did at the time, toward the group of photographs framed and hung on the wall above his desk. I had seen them many times. One was of Papa Santi, with several children gathered around him. Another was of Mama Santi, with more children. Fabio was there with children, too, and the likeness was especially good. He was laughing, of course. He seemed nearly always to be laughing that way, confidently and joyously. One could almost hear his great voice booming across the gardens.

But Emanuele and Tiofilo, who often seemed to read each other's minds, were both looking at the picture just below Fabio's, the one of a little girl, alone.

"Elisabetta!" Tiofilo exclaimed. "I think you may like to know the story of Elisabetta! It is a happy one."

"But— Fabio—" I began.

"But it is Fabio's story!" both brothers exclaimed together.

"Yes, it is Fabio's," Emanuele repeated. "And it is among the happiest. It is—what do you call it?—a success story!"

He stood up and took the picture off the wall so that I could study it more closely. She was a beautiful little girl, with gay, friendly eyes, and a warm smile. She would win friends, I thought. She looked three, perhaps four, and wore a simple cotton pinafore, the kind most of the small girls and some of the boys, too, wear at Casa Materna. I looked at the blonde curls, and it occurred to me that this child probably was not Italian.

"Yugoslavian," Emanuele said, reading my thoughts. "Our brother Fabio loved this little girl very much."

"Is she living now—somewhere, here?" I asked. My thought was to find her and talk with her.

"Very much living, Elisabetta," he assured me. "Very happy, too, and in your own country. She is an American now."

There was a long silence then, and I had time to notice how the big shadowy office contrasted a little grimly with the bright blue sky and the bright blue sea outside. Elisabetta would have enjoyed the outside better than the inside, I thought. Both the pastor and the doctor seemed to be remembering things, and there were signs of tears in Tiofilo's black eyes.

"Fabio was a lonely man, I think," he said to me. "He was so naturally a father to all little children. These children here were his, and he loved them as his own."

I knew that was true, and in my mind I saw him again with the little breadcutter, a hunchbacked boy of seven, years before. "The best bread cutter in Casa Materna!" Fabio warmly titled him, and the child grew an inch taller in that instant, although the words were actually spoken in English and he could not have known their meaning.

Again I could see Angelo, aged eight, who took a pencil from the office, and then came back in a hurry to confess. Fabio said, embracing the boy at the same time, "He is my secretary. Sometime he will need to write with skill and speed, and of course he will need pencils, many pencils. Now he makes himself useful sharpening my pencils, and he does that well." The boy, not understanding the words, had nonetheless received an accolade.

I was ready, in a way, for Elisabetta.

"Tell me the happy story," I said.

"Well, it had a sad beginning," Emanuele warned me. "You have heard of the refugee camps which Tiofilo directed after the war?"

I had, and had even visited those camps when they were filled with people. There were three of the camps near Naples, all organized and managed by Dr. Tiofilo Santi. He had tried hard to provide small employment for the older men and women, especially for the ones who could do handwork. I remembered the women around the big tables making the most beautiful embroidery.

"You may have seen with your own eyes the mother of this very Elisabetta, then!" Tiofilo told me. "She was especially skilled in the cross-stitch and made most beautiful pictures—trees, houses. Exquisite!" He gestured dramatically and I could see those trees and houses blooming in cross-stitch.

"By the grace of God we were able to save some lives in that camp," he went on, remembering.

"Georgio and the twins!" I reminded him, for Georgio had toured Naples with me only the day before.

"Georgio, yes. And Elisabetta's was another, and she was a lovely child. Fabio loved her and we called her 'Fabio's little girl.'"

Suddenly we were transported back across those years, with Italy still paralyzed over the shock of the World War II defeat, with refugees pouring in from countries even more bereft, with everyone in homes starving right along with the homeless, and Casa Materna bravely pressing to help meet the special needs of little children.

Even so long ago there was a telephone, and one of these ever-ringing phones rang sharply on an early February morning. February that year was as cold as it ever is in Italy, and Italy can be cold. There was no snow. Just bitter, biting, damp cold.

The call was for "Signore Direttore." It came from the supervisor of the refugee camp.

"Please come at once as soon as you can!" the voice said, urgently, and it was loud so that everyone in the office could hear. "It is something happening for which I must make a decision!"

"Always a decision must be made!" Fabio spoke into the telephone. "Why not make it yourself?"

"But this is a *difficult* decision!" Again the voice came sharply across the office, as if the black telephone itself were screaming. "This night—this very night—a man, Alesandro, has attempted to kill a little girl!"

Such a message indeed should crack a telephone.

"What shall I do, Signore Direttore? What shall I do?"

Fabio was in his small Fiat almost before the last words were said. Emanuele reminded me as he told the story that Fabio moved fast, and I remembered that he did, tall and big as he was. The Fiat sped on its way over the war-scarred streets to the refugee camp on the outskirts of Naples, and all along the way Fabio Santi was remembering what he knew of this family. He knew Alesandro, his wife, and the three children because he had just signed papers for their resettlement in

60

South America. They were to go in a few days. There was no problem. So why should Alesandro—

Alesandro was a Romanian, he remembered, mated, perhaps married, with a woman much younger, who was already before their marriage the mother of a little girl. Two boys had been born since. Fabio concluded that the little girl must be the one who was so nearly killed. But why would Alesandro—

"Why, indeed," Fabio asked himself. "Why would this man try to kill his step-child? And one so young." He could not quite remember the little girl, but he knew she must not be more than three years old.

The scene he found at the camp was grim. The supervisor took him directly to the room in a tent where the family stayed. It was almost empty of belongings because they were already packed to go away, and they owned so little to begin with.

The man and woman sat side by side on the ground. The woman was tearful, but silent. The man was silent, too, and distant. Two small boys clung to their mother's skirt and tried to hide. The other child, the little girl, was not there.

"Where is she?" Fabio asked. "Is she alive? Can you take me to her?"

The man seemed not to hear, or to understand. The woman drew a curtain made with a piece of blanket hung across one end of the tent. There was the child lying on the ground asleep, and there were traces of tears on her cheeks, that were white as chalk. Only her hair glowed, like gold, he thought, in the cold February sunlight. She hardly seemed alive, although she was breathing faintly.

"This child was nearly frozen!" he exclaimed. "She has been in the winter outdoors!"

The man nodded his head. "I did it!" he declared.

Fabio was shocked, and curious, too. That a man could declare so openly, and even proudly that he had tortured a little child!

The woman seemed to find a voice then.

"Signore Santi!" she cried. "Try to save us and save this little girl, Elisabetta. She is not the daughter of my husband, and he wants her dead."

"That is right," the man agreed, without shame.

She began to weep, but kept on talking desperately as if she were afraid to stop.

"This night—this cold night, he took that little girl outdoors and beat her and exposed her without clothing for so many hours."

She broke into sobs that stopped her and the man said again, "I did it." He did not seem ashamed, but eager to justify himself to the others.

"Signore Santi," he said, as one man talking to another who will understand, "Signore Santi, this is not my daughter."

Fabio saw that there was a rugged kind of integrity about the man. One could even like him. He had done what he thought was right!

"Signore Santi," he said again, frankly and as though presenting another point in a valid case at court. "She is a *girl*!"

Fabio remembered that girls are of no value in the villages. He nodded, with understanding, if not with sympathy.

"You see, Signore Santi, I have done this because I cannot earn a living for a child that is not mine, a girl that cannot work in the new country."

The man looked at his two sons with affection. Fabio said to himself that that man had done no wrong, because he did not know what he did was wrong! It was a strange thought.

The woman partly recovered from her weeping then, enough to speak again. She did not blame her husband. What he said was true. The child was not his child, and since it was a girl it could not be useful to them in the new country.

"Signore Santi," she said, "if you will take Elisabetta, I will give her to you. She is not worth much but she is mine, and if you do not take her she will die."

Fabio was both judge and attorney.

"Well, so you want to go with your husband?" he asked.

"I want to go," she said.

"He is good to you?"

"He is my husband!" She said it with pride.

"You want to leave your little girl?"

62

"I want to go," she said again. "We must live in South America, my husband and I. We cannot take care of her. Elisabetta is a burden."

"She is a human soul!" Fabio muttered, but perhaps they did not hear, or if they heard they did not understand.

The mother signed the papers at once. She kissed Elisabetta and made the Orthodox sign of the cross.

"I will never see you again," she said. "For me you are dead."
She kissed Elisabetta three times, but she was no longer weeping. There was a look that was worse than weeping.

"There is only one thing that will make a mother give up her child," Fabio said to his brothers that day. "It is love."

Dr.Tiofilo recalled these words of Fabio, as we sat in the office.

"Well, so we took Elisabetta to Casa Materna," he said. "Fabio brought her back in the Fiat that very day, and she was still asleep. There was no room, but we found room as we always do. Because, of course, we cannot deny any child. Fabio was like our father in this way." He looked at the picture of Papa Santi, with the children. "He always said, 'I do not ask how a child feels. I become that child.' And Fabio was like that, too. He *became* Elisabetta on that cold morning. She wakened from her frozen sleep at last and smiled at him, and from that time she was always smiling!"

Fabio was not the only one to care for Elisabetta. Even perfect strangers, visiting Casa Materna, noticed her among the other children and loved her. She was blonde and blue-eyed, for one thing. But the real reason that Elisabetta was noticed was her apparent delight in all people. She expected everyone who came into her world to love her, and everyone did.

Fabio Santi, from the beginning, was her favorite. She called herself, as all the others did, "Fabio's little girl," and that gentle giant loved her as if she were indeed his own daughter. Perhaps he loved her even more because he felt he had been chosen to save her life.

From that time, Tiofilo told me, Fabio's whole world was greater and more beautiful because of this child. The Casa Materna family and even the neighbors of Portici were glad for him. The Mayor of Portici had no wife, they said, and that was a pity. But he had a lovely daughter who adored him. They were seldom apart, all day long, for he liked to have her near him in his office, or when he went to the city. Tiofilo thought that these years with Elisabetta surely must have been the very happiest of his brother's life.

"I am glad that Fabio had those years!" he said.

That was the way things were when, two years later, a Colonel in the American army came to Casa Materna with his beautiful wife. Like all the others, these two fell in love with Elisabetta on the spot. They wanted her to belong to them, to make their home complete, they said, for they could not have children themselves. It happened suddenly. They wanted her very soon. They wanted her for Christmas.

Only then Fabio confessed that he himself had expected to adopt Elisabetta and become her father-by-law. The legal process was already underway, somewhat to the disapproval of the Neapolitan judge. Tiofilo smiled, remembering that problem.

"He questioned whether a Yugoslavian could become an Italian!" he exclaimed.

Fabio must have had some hard moments and days. He wanted Elisabetta to be his own. But the American Colonel and his wife had much to offer a little girl. They had a home, safety, some wealth, much love, all that a child would need. Casa Materna had love. But the American family had love, too, and what was more important, Elisabetta returned their love. They made a family, together.

"It was better," Emanuele admitted. "It was better for her to belong to them."

As director of Casa Materna, Fabio himself went to the judge in Naples to give the permission for Elisabetta to be adopted by the Americans. It was ironic then that the Neapolitan judge was the only one to disapprove of the adoption.

"But this lovely child should be an Italian!" he protested. "You are sending her to become an American!"

"Well, it is hard for you to be satisfied," Fabio told him.

And so Fabio gave his Elisabetta to the Americans. They took her to New York for Christmas.

"That was twelve years ago," Emanuele said. Elisabetta is a beautiful young lady now, and she is happy. Before Fabio died she came back to visit her Italian papa, and Fabio was never sorry for his decision."

"But he must have missed her," I said. "Did he ever adopt another child?"

Emanuele shook his head.

"Perhaps he would have done it," he said. "Fabio died too soon, you know. But perhaps he would never have found another Elisabetta." He stopped and thought. "Fabio was a lonely man, I think. But he was never sorry for his decision. And that is the happy story of Elisabetta, Fabio's little girl."

Elisabetta's picture, lying there on the desk, laughed up at us. Fabio's, on the wall above the desk, laughed, too.

I thought that perhaps the only thing that will make a father give up his beloved daughter is—love!

6. Ciro, Nunzia, Margaret, Philippo and Others

On several different visits to Casa Materna I heard brief, poignant parts of many stories. For some I came in on the final part. For others I came at the beginning and had to leave long before there would be an end in view. For some I had fragments and bits all the way through, but even these slight skeletons represented wonderful stories. I was tempted to supplement for this record, and then it occurred to me that some readers might like to complete the stories for themselves. That is the reason for "Ciro, Nunzia, Margaret, Philippo and Some Others." A professional writer would probably call these notes "raw material."

Baby Ciro

One of the most touching beginnings of stories was that of Baby Ciro whom I met several years ago when dear Papa and Mama Santi were still living and directing the Casa Materna family.

Ciro was the name of the patron saint of Naples, and St. Ciro's namesake certainly had no idea of being sad or pathetic. He was the youngest of the small children, barely past creeping age, wore little gingham pinafores and apparently enjoyed himself hugely, playing the clown for anyone who would look at him. What tore at my heart was that he only performed in pantomime. He never spoke.

I recall watching, with one of the American workers at the Casa, while some distance away the small actor went through his repertoire of foolishness.

"One wonders what can possibly be on his mind," I remarked.

"Maybe nothing at all," Sandy said, comfortably, but I couldn't drop the question so casually.

"What could have happened to keep his vocal chords locked that way," I asked. "It must have been pretty dreadful." Many of the child refugees, I knew, were unable to speak for years after the last war. They were normal in every way except for this one thing.

Sandy called to the English secretary—I believe her name was Phyllis—who was babysitting with Ciro across the way, and she walked over to our bench, with Ciro rolling along behind her. I mean to say he was literally rolling on the cement pavement. It looked painful to me, and I snatched him up from the pavement and hugged him. He wriggled and twisted, gurgling with glee. But he uttered not one word in his own or any other language.

"What is the story on Baby Ciro?" Sandy asked the secretary. "Wasn't he a sort of foundling?"

Phyllis nodded.

"It's rather a sweet little story," she said. "Not much to it, but sweet, you know. The gatekeeper found him, on Christmas morning, of all times, and on the step going into the church, of all places! I think he was there when they opened the gates, because we heard about it at breakfast. They said he was a bundle that had been pushed through the iron bars of the big gate, and sort of shoved onto the church steps. The gateman thought the person who left him might have pushed him along with a pole or something. But there he was, on Christmas morning, wrapped in a piece of sacking and sound asleep!"

She tickled him somewhere, and Ciro chuckled ecstatically.

"Good gracious, what a hustle-bustle that was!" she recalled. "Because what in the world was to be done with a year-old baby? He was too young to be put in with the others, even the smallest, and anyway there was no more room. Should they take him to the police? Should they try to find a home for him? Should they look for the parents? What should they do?"

"Apparently they didn't call the police," I remarked, and Phyllis giggled a polite English giggle.

"Indeed, no!" she said. "When did we ever do that to any child? And this was special, it being Christmas morning, and all. Fancy what Pastor Santi said, at prayers!"

"He didn't say, 'No room,' or, 'Too young,' I guess."

"Not exactly! He stood up at the breakfast table and rang the bell. You know what a little man he is—"

"Short of stature, otherwise ten feet tall," I corrected her.

"Right! Well, Papa Santi stood up looking ten feet tall, as you say, and there was this kind of expecting silence you can hear, you know. Everybody breathing sort of thing. After all it was Christmas morning. And then he told us the Christmas story, angels and all, and there was Mama Santi sitting there with that tiny thing in her lap all the while. But Pastor didn't miss a word of the story right up to the last 'Glory in the Highest!'"

"And then—"

"Well, he ended saying God had given the world a Christmas gift a long time ago, which he always says, and then he just stopped. And the silence sort of popped the way it always does and the kids screamed, 'Jesu bambino!' like that!

"And then Pastor said, 'Well, God has given Casa Materna a special Christmas present today!' He took that tiny thing from Mama Santi and held him up in the air all skin and bones and big black eyes, and would you believe, grinning like a little hyena! Poor baby. I cried. I couldn't help it."

"What did the children do?" I asked.

"Oh, they were thrilled. Everybody loves a baby. They promised to take care of him all around the clock."

"And you never learned who he was or where he came from?"

"No. We tried. Of course I always thought it was someone who knew Casa Materna well—the one who left him, you know. Pushing that bundle over onto the church steps, and on Christmas morning, was just too pat. But we never heard another word. And the *pauvre enfant* had a rough time. He was sick and had worms and diarrhea and about everything a baby can have, but babies always pull through the most amazing things. He was sort of marked, too, as if he'd been bumped rather a lot."

"And he's never talked at all?"

"Never a word in two whole years! The doctor says he probably will speak sometime, of course."

"Do you ever wonder what he will say?" I asked.

She shuddered.

"I hope, in a way, that I won't be here," she began.

68

At that moment Baby Ciro shrieked and began hammering on my shoulder. Apparently he had had enough of not being looked at. I chucked him under his two chins and he was immediately happy. There appeared not to be a cloud in those enormous sparkling black eyes. But I wondered what dark secrets might lie back of them, and far back of consciousness.

I do not know where Baby Ciro is now, or when he left Casa Materna, and I have no idea what he said, or if he ever did speak. But I am told that children who have this handicap and overcome it later, seldom say anything significant.

Nunzia and Her Dentisto

In other parts of the world, but not in Naples, some people have already forgotten the Second World War when both Naples and Portici were bombed, and the years following when American soldiers occupied the streets and public buildings. Among them were many who found their way to Casa Materna, loved the children, and finally helped to rebuild parts of the home which had been destroyed by American bombs.

Nunzia's dentist was one of these. He happened to be an African American, which might have made a difference in his own country but went unnoticed in Naples. The refugee years for Casa Materna had been especially hard on teeth, and Dr. Young was a busy dentist. He was also handsome, young and popular. He loved all the children as they loved him, but Nunzia was his favorite, and he was hers. The people at Casa Materna thought of him as "Nunzia's dentisto."

After the occupation when the young dentist left with the rest of the American army and went home to New Orleans to practice, his little friend was bereft. She did not forget her good dentist, nor did the dentist forget his Nunzia. Postcards and parcels came back to Italy, many at first, fewer as time went on, but always Nunzia was overjoyed when the post brought some word from America. Always she sent some word back. After a while she was even able to write letters in a big round hand, to thank him.

Two, three, perhaps five years went by. For a long time there had been no message from America. The grown-ups, when they thought of it at all, considered that the young soldier must have forgotten, surely, and it was not to be wondered at. America is so far away. They are busy in America. Nunzia herself no longer talked about him. They considered that that chapter in her life story must have ended.

But then, suddenly, without any letter to announce it, another package arrived. It was rather a large one, with a great many stamps.

This is where I came into the story, because I was lucky enough to be there when the package came and when Nunzia opened it. That was a great occasion.

The package was placed in a prominent place on the big desk in the office and lay there in splendor. Nunzia was told that it was there, and that she might go into the office and open the package. She came in softly, on tip-toe, and alone. She hesitated, looked all about the big room, and then as though attracted by a magnet, her eyes turned to the desk. I wondered if she would notice me, a stranger, back in a far corner, but I might have been another chair. Her eyes never left the desk, and with every step forward she smiled more wondrously. I thought I heard her say, "Dentisto!" and others watching from the doorway thought so, too. But she whispered it.

When Nunzia at last reached the desk and touched the package, she did so gently, almost hesitantly. It was as though what she was about to do was a holy act and must be done carefully, with respect and reverence. Slowly she lifted off and folded layer by layer each precious piece of wrapping. At last the large white box was naked. She waited then for an eager second before putting out both hands to take the lid off the box. There was a glimpse for us of lace and ruffles, brightly colored, and at last she held up for all to see two lovely little dresses, one pink, the other blue, both with white ruffles. Both were selected with loving care by someone who remembered and loved a tiny girl.

That was what touched me so deeply that I wiped away tears which Nunzia of course never saw. The dresses were for a tiny girl. Nunzia, in those five years, had grown to be a big girl!

The mistake worried no one except me. There are ways of doing things to dresses, and if the dresses could not be fixed, then there were tiny girls to fit tiny dresses. For Nunzia herself the delight of receiving and opening a present from her dentist in America would always be greater than the satisfaction of wearing the contents. But what touched me was the thought that years go by and little girls grow big, and that an American dentist had forgotten how a clock, even an Italian clock, will not stand still!

Remembering this little piece of a story of Nunzia, I did some research rather recently and discovered the very dentist of the story, much alive and practicing in New Orleans. I had a letter from Dr. Young, enclosing the note which he had received from Nunzia those years ago. It was short and in a round, childish hand. It said, "Thank you for the dresses," in Italian.

The dentist wrote to me that he would like Nunzia's letter returned to him because it is all he has now of his little Italian friend. He would like to know where she is now, and if she is married. And he would like to keep the letter she wrote him thanking him for the dresses. I have returned the letter, but I cannot tell him what has happened to Nunzia.

Margaret and Charles

I discovered the picture of these two among some other photographs in the office files and carried it to dinner one evening to ask Louisa Santi about them. Margaret and Charles contrasted oddly, I thought, with names like Peppo and Angel, and I was interested, too, in their faces. They were much darker than most Italians, even the ones from the south. Their eyes were sloe-like, quiet, not sparkling like Italian eyes, but deep and mysterious.

Louisa remembered them well. Emanuele did, also, and there exploded at once an exciting Italian exchange of opinion, memory, feeling. Both talked fast at the same time, disagreeing and agreeing with equal violence and with most wonderful gestures. From the English that was mixed in with Italian I gathered that Louisa was perfectly sure Margaret and Charles were five and seven when they

71

came, and when that picture was made. Emanuele remembered distinctly that they were four and six, and that the picture was made later. He recalled the moment, the very instant, in fact, when he had seen them in the church in Naples. He remembered exactly how he had gone to the very inner city hovel where they lived, and it was a room behind the Naples convent. He settled the argument by declaring that we would go on Sunday to the very spot and look at the room.

"Another family will live there now," he told me. "But we shall see the very place."

On Sunday morning, therefore, we climbed into the Fiat and went to church in Naples. I saw there the very pew in which he had first seen those two with their mother, a beautiful woman, an Italian. The children I was sure were not Italian, and I was right. They had come from Calcutta. Their father was an Anglo-Indian.

After church we proceeded on, as planned, to see the very room where they had lived. Up one street of Naples, and then another, we rode, moving slowly and more slowly until we stopped altogether, parked the car and walked the rest of the way. There was simply too much living on the street to let a car go through, Emanuele explained to me. But even on foot we had to push our way among the washing and shoe shining and baby nursing that was briskly underway on a Sunday noontime.

Our stopping place was halfway up a steep and narrow crowded street, before a home that might easily have been a shop, like the ones on either side. The door was one that pulled up, exposing the whole room, which we could see was also the whole home. A woman was lying on the bed. A man was rocking in the one chair.

I felt embarrassed at intruding, but Emanuele was not, and apparently there was no need. Spontaneous hospitality, I have noticed is a characteristic of all Italian homes, rich or poor, and although Emanuele, in an English aside to me, deplored the obvious poverty of this home and this family, I couldn't discover that they felt apologetic.

Almost before we had stopped, the man was jumping up to offer his chair. He was bearded, but I think he was young, under the beard. He called in both directions, and several children came running from up and down the street. I assumed they belonged there, but I never knew how many there were because they kept appearing and disappearing. The woman who had been lying on the bed, obviously pregnant, was on her feet as fast as her husband, and flourishing a coffee pot.

Emanuele refused both chair and coffee for us both, and began talking immediately with the man. Occasionally he interspersed a comment in English, to me, but most of the talk was in Italian. I had a chance to look around the home and to try to make a little conversation with the woman, who stood with the coffee pot in her hand, smiling at me. I tried to tell her that she should not stand but couldn't seem to make her understand.

I have yet to see an Italian home, however poor, that has not some kind of effort at beauty about it. Italians seem to put their hearts into their homes, and when the home is only one room, perhaps the heart is even more prominent.

This one had a lava rock floor, which nothing much could be done about, but the walls were hung with bright pictures of saints, and the usual small altar, with its crisp lace-edged white covering and its candles, stood on one side. The round table was spread with a beautifully embroidered table cover, and in the back of the room there was a cupboard with a looking glass tacked to its door, and I could see myself even from so far away. The bed—there was only one—had a pink lace bedspread and was neatly made up.

"Five people sleep on that bed," Emanuele told me. "Of course not all of the five are always sleeping at the same time."

His conversation with the man in the rocking chair was brief and we hurried away rather quickly, with the children clustering around in the open doorway to say good-bye. There were warm invitations to come back. But I noticed that the pregnant mother fell back on the bed as we left. She must have been exhausted.

"With the new baby coming they must give up one of the children," Emanuele explained to me. "We will take the oldest boy. You did not see him. He sells orange drink in the square on Sundays when he can get a chance. The man has no job. He is a carpenter, but there is no work for him."

"Where in the world do they do the cooking for that crowd?" I asked.

He gestured up and down the street, and it occurred to me for the first time that the small charcoal stoves here and there, which I had thought were for special things like roasting peanuts to sell, had to do with plain everyday living and eating, with spaghetti and spinach most evident in the cooking posts we passed.

"It is cold in the winter to live half outdoors," Emanuele said, as if he had read my thoughts.

"And that is the place where you found the Indian children?" I remarked.

"Margaret and Charles? Yes, that is the very spot where they lived. But it is a palace now compared with then," he said.

We went on down the street, pushing our way through the people, closely followed by those children belonging to the home we had just visited, until we came to the place where we had left the Fiat. It was still there, surpisingly ignored by the children playing around it. We sat in the car, with the children sitting by the side of the street sometimes looking at us, while Emanuele told me more about Margaret and Charles.

"The Italian mother of these two children appeared in the Protestant church, as I have told you," he said. "It was on a Sunday morning, and it was a surprise, because not many new ones come in this Catholic city. This woman was noticed, and those children were noticed, too. They had nice dresses. They did not look poor. But they were not Italian!"

Emanuele made a special effort to speak to the woman at the close of the service and asked her directly if the children belonged to her.

"She explained her whole story to me then and there," he told me. "She had been a Catholic but had not been faithful for many years. And then there appeared this Anglo-Indian, a Protestant. They were married, and she went back to Calcutta where he lived. There the children were born, both more Indian than Italian or English. And then she returned to Italy with the children because her husband was ill. She hoped to find a job and bring him to Italy, too. She thought he might get well if he were in Italy."

"I suppose an Anglo-Indian, married to an Italian, would really be in a spot," I said. "And the children certainly wouldn't be happy in Calcutta."

"Exactly," said Emanuele. "And so I went at her invitation to her home, and it was in this place, the very place you saw. But what you saw was a rich home compared with hers. She had no bed at all. These children had nothing, not even food. I can tell you that I have lived among poor people in a poor city for most of my life, and I have never seen a place as poor as this. These people would soon have died. They had nothing."

"But nice clothes, to come to church," I remembered.

"But that was sad, too!" he said. "Their Italian mother wished them to look nice in Italy. She hid them in this place while she got a job cleaning floors, and for lira totaling perhaps fifteen dollars a month. She used the first pay, every lira, for clothes for the children to wear to church that day. And they had no breakfast, either!"

"And that was the day you met them!"

"The very day, and all those weeks before she had left them when she went to work. Those two little ones stayed alone in that bare room. It was touching," he recalled. "The boy was his sister's keeper!"

After that, he told me, Charles and Margaret came to live at Casa Materna, while their mother continued to work faithfully and to save what she earned, until there was enough money to bring the father home from India.

"And so it ended happily with a reunion?" I asked.

He shook his head.

"No, it was sad," he said. "The woman wrote to her husband to say that there was money now for his passage to Italy. He might come at once. But then it was a long time and the letter had no answer at all."

"No answer?" I said. "Had the man deserted them?"

"Not at all. For after a while the word came from the government of that province in India, and there is nothing so cold as a letter from the government! It said the father had already died. He was very ill, you know, when the woman and the children came here to live."

"And there was no reunion?"

"No reunion."

I spent a moment thinking of the grief and disappointment of that woman, after all of her waiting and working and saving.

"But what about the children, then?" I asked finally.

"In a way they were lucky," he answered. "Those two were happy at Casa Materna. And that made their mother happy, too. They only left finally when they were able to help her a little. But they called Casa Materna always their home. Even when the girl became a secretary and the boy an electrician, they thought of this as their home."

I looked at those beautiful, dark sloe-eyes, for I had brought the picture along with me that day.

"Did the Indian children ever feel different from the Italians because they looked so different?" I asked.

"Who knows what a child feels?" he asked. "How can I say? We are all different. At Casa Materna we are many races. We might say everybody is different. And yet we are all the same!"

He started the car, and we rode back to Casa Materna. It was already long past dinner time.

Constanza and Phillipo

My interest in the Indian children reminded Emanuele and his sister Louisa of two other children who were "different." Louisa especially wanted me to know the story of the two from the Congo, because in that story Casa Materna played the hard role of family reuniting. As I think of it now, the story of Constanza and Phillipo does not reflect creditably on some aspects of some missionary life, to be sure, but as Louisa says, "Missionaries are people, too."

It seems there was an Italian missionary, a widow in Congo, who had one son. Perhaps he was spoiled. Perhaps he was neglected. At any rate, that boy seemed to have no anchors, and at the young age of eighteen he married a Congolese girl, a student in the school where his mother was a teacher. The couple was supported by the missionary mother, who accepted the union with a surprising amount of grace in the beginning. By the time the boy was twenty-one and his wife nineteen, there were two children, and these were our Constanza and Phillipo.

Just about this time there was some sort of scandal, perhaps a political one, and the young man and his African wife were outsted from that troubled country, Congo. They fled to Rome where a third child was born.

But in Rome things went from bad to worse. The young man either couldn't or wouldn't make a living. His Congolese wife accused him of laziness. He accused her of unfaithfulness. And finally both of them were discovered, with their three children, sleeping on the steps of a church in Rome, because they had not even a room to live in.

And this is the place where Casa Materna entered the story. Louisa told me that a Salvation Army officer discovered them there on the church steps. As she said, it was lucky for them that it was summer, since they slept outdoors. The officer sent word to Casa Materna because he knew about the home, and Dr. Tiofilo drove immediately to Rome to bring the children back with him. The young baby stayed with the mother. They were not sure just what would be done about the family, but it was clear that the boy and girl must have some home other than the church steps.

"But you should have seen them!" Louisa said to me. "I suppose we have never had two lovelier children here. *As* lovely, yes, but no lovelier."

"Were they accepted by the other children?" I asked.

"Well, that was rather funny," she said. "You see, these two were very black! And do you know the Italian children were simply delighted! They were in danger of being killed with kindness, those two, and spoiled with attention!"

"Discrimination in reverse, maybe," I said, skeptically. "Did the Italians sort of think it was their Christian duty to be kind to the black children?"

She stared at me.

"Christian duty?" she asked wonderingly. "I don't know whether these children know about Christian duty. I doubt if they would know what that means. But children are attracted to what is different. I think that was it. The black ones they thought were so much more beautiful and rare than brown and white ones!"

"What about the parents?" I asked. "Did you ever hear from them?"

"Of course!" she said. "Too much we heard! I sometimes think children would be better off without the interference of parents! They both came to visit but not together. They played—what do you say?— tug of war! All of us dreaded a visit from either one of them. The two children dreaded a visit. Each parent wanted to make them hate the other parent!"

"And what about the missionary grandmother? Did you hear from her, too?"

"Of course! And that was another nuisance," she recalled. "That woman wrote letters from Africa, trying to take the children for herself. She accused the mother of being a prostitute even before the marriage in Congo. She said the girl had falsely named her son as the father of the first child, Constanza, and forced the marriage. Indeed, Constanza is very black, as that woman pointed out."

"What a spot you were in, then!" I exclaimed. "Did she try to take the children by force?"

"Well, my brother Fabio was a lawyer, you know," she assured me. "But the problem of Casa Materna was to reunite that family. For us it was not important what had been before, but what ought to be and could be in the future."

"Good social work principles," I said.

"Exactly. It was important to us that these children should continue to love and respect both father and mother. That was our problem."

"And did you succeed?"

"Not at once. In fact it seemed that we might not succeed. That young mother somehow got the money to go back to Congo."

"By soliciting?"

"Who knows? She got the money, and then she wanted to go, and that was natural, I suppose."

"And she took the two children?"

"No. She left Constanza and Phillipo here with us. She took the new baby."

"But why did she leave the others so close to their father?" I asked. "Couldn't they have traveled free?"

She smiled. "They could, of course. They were only babies. But I think that young mother knew they were better off here at Casa Materna. And there was always the grandmother in Congo, you know."

"True. And so they stayed here."

"They stayed. And of course had here in Italy another part of this little family, you remember."

I had indeed forgotten that unfortunate young father, back in Rome.

"After his wife went to Congo, perhaps he came to himself. Perhaps he even missed her, and was sorry. Perhaps he was strengthened by love for the children. But he did get a job, as a painter."

"Oh, an artist?" I asked.

"A painter of houses, not pictures," she corrected me. "And do you know I think if his mother had not always expected that young man to become a scholar or a diplomat, or someone important, he might have been better from the beginning, and happier! He was a fine painter. Now, when he came to see the children, he was a different father. They adored him. And we at Casa Materna were glad to have him come. We looked forward and wondered even if there might be a place for him here, as a painter!"

"Wonderful!" I said, anticipating. "So it all ended happily!"

"Not all at once," she said. "There was not enough painting here. But he continued to work, and the children continued to stay at Casa Materna. They needed a mother."

"Did he marry again?" I asked. "An Italian girl?"

"I think it never occurred to that man to marry!" she declared. "It is true he was spoiled and maybe he was lazy. But there was something in that missionary background perhaps. I don't think he would have been unfaithful to his wife!" She nodded firmly.

"And then there was the other thing. In spite of all the quarreling and in spite of all the things he had said against her, that man loved the young Congolese woman!" She nodded again, not so vigorously. "It is my sincere conviction, too, that he knew all the time that she was not really a bad woman. I believe she had always been good. And then these problems are unimportant if you compare them against the facts of love and responsibility! Do you know what happened?"

"I can guess," I said.

"Exactly, you are right. He saved his money, that man, and then he came to Casa Materna one day and gathered those children and their dolls and toys and took them back to Congo to their mother."

"It must have cost a lot of money," I said. "Do painters make a good deal here?"

"Casa Materna helped to make it possible," she admitted. "We thought it was wise. Children need a mother if it is possible. But we shall always be a little poorer here without Constanza and Phillipo."

The last word was that the family was together, and apparently even that weird grandmother had had a change of heart. They all lived happily!

We looked at the picture again. They were very black, as Louisa had said. Those black eyes, however, were different from the sloe-eyes of the Indians. They were merry and mischievous.

"We have had beautiful children here," Louisa said again. "But not one child was more beautiful than these two!"

This skeleton of a story is one I would love to reconstruct!

7. The Long Way to Corso Garibaldi

Ischia and Roberto are inseparably linked in my mind.

Ischia is the large island that appears like a great shadow on the right of the horizon as one looks across Naples Bay from Casa Materna. On cloudy days the shadow even disappears. The Arabs found the island in ancient times, which accounts for the many clay buildings, painted pink and blue. The Germans found it during World War II, and many of the shops have German names. Ischia has a castle ruin all its own. And a good many people think that this island may be the best substitute for heaven that can be found on earth.

We had a gold and blue day on Ischia, Roberto and I. He was bent on teaching me to swim, although I explained with signs, and demonstrated with inept performance, that swimming is not my field. If Roberto got the message he was not impressed. But we did have an understanding. I presented him with my thong sandals which he admired and which fit him, and he gave me in return half a stick of chewing gum begged from a vendor on the beach. We chewed together, and Roberto was in a state of bliss all day long, including the boat ride home at twilight.

But I think perhaps the best feature about Ischia, to Roberto's way of thinking, was its nearness to Casa Materna. I will not forget that boat ride home, when he ran wildly from port to starboard and bow to stern like a drunken cricket, and finally in impassioned ecstasy demanded of me that I *look*! And that I take a "fotografia" of a red spot over on the mainland shore. "Immediatamente!"

"What is it?" I asked. He needed no translation, nor did I when he screamed in rapture, "Bella! Casa Materna!"

And so beautiful Ischia, paradise and all, was behind us, dismissed and forgotten while all the wonder of earth and high heaven was centered in one red spot on the Italian coast line. Casa Materna!

Anyway, after that remarkable day I went about learning all I could concerning Roberto.

It was not difficult to exhaust the sources of information, but I did learn enough to explain for me the curiously adult way this boy had of peering out at me and all the world around him, through his pale blue eyes. It was as though he had become old before he learned to be young, and I found this to be true. I wrote the two stories which follow from a few cold facts in the Casa Materna files, and from reminiscences of some of the Casa Materna staff. I have written it as a fiction story because it was interesting and convenient to do so, but the facts are true, and Roberto, the young musician, is still at Casa Materna.

Roberto

The distance from Via Porto to Corso Garibaldi is a long walk, and it was not strange that Roberto should be weary, for he was only nine, technically still a bambino. Also, he carried a small parcel which seemed to grow larger and heavier.

But although the distance seemed long to his legs, it seemed hardly long enough, to Roberto's mind. There was a great deal of thinking to be done before he reached Corso Garibaldi, and he had even to slow his steps to consider a few matters.

There was the question of why he was going in the first place. It was necessary to leave the home of his grandmother because his sister Firenza slept in the bed with the old woman, and the bed was too small for three, so there was no room for him on the bed. Or so she said. Yet in some places, and Roberto had seen them, one bed might hold five—six—even nine people. And maybe the problem was not so much the room on the bed after all. For one thing the old woman need not reach so wide when she slept. There was surely enough space for a small boy.

The truth came to him in a great light after the candy incident. It was all tied up with the fifty lira and the dolce—that sticky, sweet dessert that was almost candy.

She was angry, that old woman, when Roberto found fifty lira lying in the street like a gift from heaven. And what should he do with it except to buy dolce for his little sister! But how that old woman had screamed like a factory whistle.

"Fifty lira to throw away for dolce! There is no money for bread. There is no money for shoes. But plenty for dolce!" she scolded. And how she looked! Like an ugly hen!

And what had happened then?

"Well, then, here is your dolce!" Firenza had said reluctantly, with the grandmother's eye fixed sternly upon her. But he could see one tear or it might be two. Firenza was fond of sweets. And slowly she opened a small sticky hand and held it out to him.

So what was there to do? The dolce was no longer good to eat any more. He turned his head away from them both, and she dropped it on the street. Fifty lira's worth!

So now he was leaving the home of his grandmother, with all his possessions tied in a package. He was already passing by the small shop of his friend Vittorio, who had sold him the candy for Firenza.

"More dolce, my friend?" Vittorio inquired. Roberto's find on Via Porto was not forgotten by the shop keeper! "Any more lira falling from heaven for you, lucky one?"

"Not so lucky," Roberto answered. "Not so lucky at all. No lira."

"Well, where do you go with the package?" Vittorio asked. "And already for church although it is only Thursday?" Count on Vittorio to see the package and to notice Roberto's other suit that he wore only to church although it was not much better than the one he wore every day.

"Well, I might be going away for a while," he said, as if he did that often and it were not unusual at all.

"Going away?" Vittorio's eyes grew soft and he looked into the back room where his wife stayed most of the time. "Tonetta, our young friend Roberto is going away!"

Tonetta must have been listening behind the curtain in the back of the shop! She rushed out, hugged Roberto hard and kissed him on one cheek and then the other.

"Going away?" she cried. "Where do you go, little one?"

"To—to a place," Roberto said. Then in a burst of confidence he told them, for he liked Tonetta and Vitorio. "To Casa Materna!" he said.

"It is a good place," Vittorio said soberly. "You are right."

"But you need a present!" Tonetta said eagerly, thrusting some pieces of dolce into his hand. "And God will take care of you. It is a good place."

That made Roberto feel good. He put a piece of the candy in his mouth and picked up the package, which did not feel so heavy now. As he hurried along, without looking back, he thought he heard Tonetta say softly to her husband, "Poor bambino."

But he had a great deal more thinking to do before he would reach Corso Garibaldi.

All right, then, so his grandmother was jealous. She wanted Firenza for herself. All that about the bed was made up and a lie. There was plenty of room, and he had always slept with his mother and father and Firenza, the four of them together, in the same bed. But there was more to it than just a bed, because he had slept on the floor for some time, and she did not like him any better.

The floor was stone, but he got used to it, and he would have liked staying there well enough if that were the only problem. Nor did he object to the working. She had said if he must stay with her and eat all of her bread like a porcilina, and crowd her small room, then certainly he must work.

Sweeping and scrubbing was the work he found to do. Sometimes he was paid a little, and all the lira he made went straight back to his grandmother, but it was never enough to please her. That old woman hated him. She was jealous for one thing. But there was more.

The new idea had come to him in the night, on the cold floor, and not so long ago, either. It had come to him that his troubles with his grandmother were connected with his father and mother. But he was not ready to think of his father, or his mother, or that other one, the "uncle." All that was shut away as if it were behind a door. Sometime, maybe rather soon, it would be necessary to open the door. Maybe when he was ten? He was almost ten, now. But there was a war going on all the time inside Roberto. The thoughts wanted to open the door and come out, and he did not want them to.

It seemed a good idea, walking along this way, to stop and say hello now to Signora Nangano, and to smell the bread baking there. Sometimes she gave him a piece and it was delicious.

"Buon giorno, Signora!" he called, pushing aside the bead strings that made a pretty curtain over the doorway. The lovely warm smell of the bread rushed out to him.

"Buon giorno!" came the answer from back there, and then the little room shook when she came running. Signora Nangano was fat and jolly with extra chins that shook when she laughed or cried, but mostly she laughed. She always talked in a loud voice as if she meant all the people in the street to hear every word distinctly.

"Buon giorno, my little one!" she said again. "Poor bambino, how are you?"

She kissed him energetically on both cheeks.

"How is your little sister?" She looked at him sharply. "And the old woman, your grandmother. How is she?"

Signora Nangano did not ask about his father and mother. No one ever asked about them. Everyone said, "Poor bambino!"

"They are all well, I think," Roberto said politely. "My sister Firenza and my grandmother are all right."

"And you, with the little bundle. Where do you go, then?" she asked.

"Well, I am going to Casa Materna," he told her.

She nodded thoughtfully, and her eyes grew soft and moist as Vittorio's had done.

"How is that?" she asked. "Did your grandmother put you out?"

"I preferred to go," he answered with dignity. "I am old enough and there is no room in my grandmother's house."

Signora's eyes filled with real tears.

"Poor baby," she said again. "No room!" She muttered so he could not quite understand, but it sounded like, "There is plenty of room! Plenty!" She blew her nose on her apron.

"Well, they will give you good care at Casa Materna," she said finally. "I hear the children are happy there. I hear it is the happiest place in Portici, and they are always singing. They are not Catholics there, but they are good."

Of course you cannot stay all day visiting a busy woman who bakes bread for a living. Roberto thought it was time for him to be going.

"It is a long walk to Casa Materna," he remarked, picking up his bundle again. "It is all the way to Corso Garibaldi. I only stopped for this minute."

She was going back to the oven, he noticed, and what a smell that was when she opened the oven door.

"You will take a small loaf of bread," she insisted, pulling it out expertly, with tongs, and then wrapping it quickly in a piece of paper. "Show them at Casa Materna what good bread we make on Via Porto! And then," she reached in her pocket and brought a small purse. "You will need some lira, too."

She took out a one thousand lira note that smelled of the fresh bread. Roberto's eyes nearly popped out. A thousand lira for *him*! His hand trembled as he reached to take it from her.

"If there is a charge at Casa Materna," she explained, "you can pay them then."

He hadn't thought of there being a charge, and it was a good idea she had.

"Well, grazie!" he said. She kissed him on both cheeks again.

"Ciao!" she said, as the bead strings fell behind him. She said something else which he was not meant to hear, but he did hear very plainly because she talked in a loud voice even when she meant to whisper.

"Poor bambino!" said Signora Nangano, just as Tonetta had said it.

But he was on his way again, and there were still more things to think about before he would arrive at Corso Garibaldi.

There was his father, and there were those times when his father was happy. The closed door of his mind began to open a little. Firenza would hardly remember the happy times, he thought, because she had been so small. In those days it was like sunlight all the time. Later, when his father was mostly angry, then it was as though storm clouds had come over a fair sky. Firenza would run to hide then, and Roberto hoped she would not remember how she had hidden from her father's anger. Roberto, being a boy, did not hide. He only looked down at the stones of the floor and stood silently. He did not run away even when his father hit him. Perhaps his father could not help it. The thing Roberto wanted to say now to his father was how much he felt love for him, and sadness and shame. The sadness and shame were because of what Roberta knew and yet did not know, either. It was very strange.

The way to Corso Garibaldi was too short after all! It was almost accomplished, and still he was not ready. Still there was more thinking to do.

There was that old woman, and how she had used to spit in the direction of the prison! When the wind would blow, he remembered, he caught the full wet force of it in his face.

"Damn you, old woman!" he had screamed.

He screamed it now, forgetting for a moment that he was on the way to Corso Garibaldi. He was in fact passing by the shop of Peppito, the little shoe maker.

Quickly remembering, Roberto bowed to Peppito, who sat outside the door tailor fashion, hammering on a shoe sole. Peppito looked at him reproachfully, Roberto thought, although he was deaf as a stone, and surely could not have heard what Roberto had screamed.

"I was thinking—about an old woman," he explained anyway, although Peppito could not hear thunder.

Peppito nodded, and smiled, and Roberto went on, walking much more slowly now, because Corso Garibaldi was not very far any more.

Well, there was his mother. The shut door opened a little farther for him to think about his mother. Thinking of her now, Roberto was warm and excited and forgot how his legs ached. It was not because she was beautiful, although he thought she must be. But there was something else. It was a brightness, a way to make you feel gay. She laughed. She danced. She took his hands and they skipped together. She held him close and he was ecstatic. And in all this abundant joy, the baby Firenzsa smiled and gurgled and belched in her crib.

"Ah, ah!" his mother sang like a bird, and they romped, like children, she and Roberto, and he felt like the older of the two. Like a bird she was, a bright, feathered parakeet bird. Later on she was like a parakeet in a cage, in a way.

Roberto could not quite recall, because it was so long ago, when he had begun to feel shame, guilt, in all this pleasure. When he began to know that there was something like a ship sailing between his mother whom he loved and his father whom he loved, it was as if to love the one were disloyalty to the other. It was that kind of feeling.

So there was another person to think about before he could reach Corso Garibaldi. The other person was the uncle.

Now Roberto had never had an uncle of his own in all the nine years of his life. Nearly every other boy and girl he knew had at least one, and he knew about uncles and approved of them. Perhaps he even wished for one. And suddenly there was one for him. For Firenza, too, but more for him because she was so small that she would know nothing about uncles.

"This is your uncle," his mother had said.

That was all right, wasn't it? But he was not sure. He had to go to the square to play, now, and take Firenza with him, whether he wanted to or not. When he protested, the parakeet hit him. The uncle never hit him or paid attention to him. There was hardly reason to hate the uncle. But Roberto did hate him.

In the end the uncle vanished. After the great trouble he was gone and Roberto never saw him again. So it was foolish to hate the uncle. To hate anybody is hard. To waste the big business of hating on somebody who is gone and may even be dead is foolish. Especially it is foolish when hating him is the only thing that keeps him with you. But Roberto did hate him.

There was still more to think about, but the way to Corso Garibaldi was accomplished, and the number he looked for was close. It was 2-3-5. His father had whispered it to him. How long ago? It seemed like a long time. It was before the policeman came. It was even before— He remembered the number for a long time.

He stopped at last, breathed heavily, hesitated, and then pressed his finger on the buzzer. The great iron gate swung open, and he walked under the stone arch of Casa Materna.

"Pronto!" he shouted boldly. "Pronto! Where is the keeper?"

The man standing there was not the keeper of the gate, but the Pastor, although of course Roberto did not know that. It was Thursday afternoon, and that was the day for church. Roberto did not know that, either, or that the church was right there by the gate.

"I wish to see the important man," Roberto said firmly. "The head!"

The man put out his hand and took Roberto's.

"There are no important men here," he said. "Or women. But we are all alike. My name is Santi. What can I do for you?"

"The Pastor!" Roberto exclaimed. "Signore Direttore!"

"Right!" The man's eyes twinkled. Roberto could hardly be afraid of anyone so friendly.

"Well, my name is Roberto," he said hesitantly, and then more boldly, "I have come to live with you here. I will work for you, and I work well."

"That is good," said the Pastor. "We like good workers. We like to play, too. But why have you come to Casa Materna?"

The moment was here. He had never said it before, aloud, and yet in his mind he had been practicing for a long time. And he had been preparing, of course, all the way to Corso Garibaldi today. He had been preparing in fact ever since—

The Pastor was listening, with earnest attention.

My name is Roberto," he said again. But he had already told the Pastor his name. "My mother is dead. My father is in prison. My grandmother has no room in her house for—" He stopped and the Pastor nodded thoughtfully.

"No room for the son of a murderer," Roberto said firmly. He was surprised and pleased to hear how well he spoke the words he had never said aloud before. "My father killed my mother. With a knife. I saw. But it was right because my mother was unfaithful."

It was done in half a moment, and after that Roberto felt easy and smiled. He must have done well, he thought. Could the Pastor—

89

could anyone tell from the outside about the war that was going on inside? He thought not. He could close the door now for a long time. Later he would open the door again and look through those thoughts inside. But not yet.

The pastor smiled and took his hand again.

"It is Thursday, you know," he said. "On Thursday we have church. You will like the singing. All the Casa Materna family likes to sing praise to God."

The Pastor

In the room that opened on the terrace and looked out to the sea, the Pastor that night watched twilight fall across Naples Bay and saw the lights of the city begin to blossom like gold flowers against the sky, and beyond those lights the dimmer lights of Ischia. He talked aloud to himself, as he did sometimes.

"What did this boy say?" he asked himself, and answered his own question. "But of course. His father had been taken to prison."

It was not a new story for the Pastor to hear. Unfaithfulness. Violence. The husband. The lover. One of the oldest of human stories. And never less tragic for its being told so often. Always, he thought, the innocent must suffer. Always the sins of the fathers are laid on the child. And when the child begins to understand what he has always known—then the real tragedy begins.

And what about this new boy, Roberto? No emotion at all in his clear, calm statement there in the gateway. Not a sign of a tear. This was the saddest of all, that a child should be so old, and so disciplined, and so wise in the evil of the world.

On his knees then, almost in sight of the place where St. Paul first stopped in Italy, Pastor Santi prayed, "O Signore, thou who knowest the deeds of men and the deepest hearts of little children, see this child. Find for him compassion. Discover for him the way of weeping."

And then the Pastor wept himself. Yes, he wept wet tears. Italians are not ashamed of tears. Maybe this is why they have been able to bear so much.

The lights of Naples glittered across the bay. A few bright, crisp December stars gleamed steadily from a sky now navy blue.

The Pastor liked to play his violin, a very special one, a Stradivarius, and to speak to God with music, but it was not often that he let the instrument speak at this time of night when the children were sleeping overhead.

But sometimes when his heart was especially heavy, and he needed a more direct way to God, he played at night. He did this night.

Out over the waters, dark blue now like the sky, and up toward the still, cold stars, the prayer went, sweet and sharp, and up and around it crept and swirled, in through the open windows, filling the great rooms where the children slept upstairs, going high, high to the twenty-foot ceilings, and back again, enfolding and surrounding every small bunk bed, upper and lower deck.

Of course children sleep hard after a good supper. Roberto, the new boy, slept with the others. His job, for the day, was well done, and he was well fed, too. None of them wakened, nor did he, but he may have dreamed and in the dream he may have caught the message of the music. He may have caught the prayer on its way, as a short wave radio will catch the broadcast on its way to some far off receiving station.

"Show this child the way to compassion! Help him to weep! Find for him purpose."

8. Roberto, the Musician

When he tried afterward to remember those first days at Casa Materna, Roberto found that he could not because they blurred together and got lost. But a few facts stood out, by themselves.

First, there was room for him.

There was a bed, his own bed, all to himself, with a mattress and a blanket, and this was a wonderful fact for a boy who had never slept in a bed that was not shared with two or three others and who recently had slept on a stone floor.

But then there was another fact which surprised him. He discovered that one bed, all to himself, was a little lonely. He astonished himself by feeling lonesome for the stone floor of his grandmother!

To be sure there were other boys in the same room at night, but they were in other beds, and although he could hear them talking and could talk himself, he could not touch another person without climbing out of bed. But it helped a good deal to talk. At night Roberto would keep brushing his teeth in the bathroom as long as there was somebody to brush with and to be close to. And then he would try, after the lights were out, to keep talking as long as anybody would listen or answer back. It was lonesome in the dark when the talking, and then the whispering, finally stopped, for then he was alone. He thought that this must be among the hardest things in the world, to be alone.

A maze of many faces, dark and light and nearly always kind, began to break up into different faces, and to become Guilio, and Giovanna, and others. He could even see Giovanna's face by itself, black eyes, shining black hair, much like Firenza's. And there was Emilio who was different because he had red hair and was spattered with freckles all over.

Something inside Roberto persisted in reminding him that these were strangers all around him, and strangers were not to be trusted, only to be talked to as if you knew everything and felt easy. But even so, he began to notice that these strangers apparently didn't distrust him, as he felt they ought to.

Food was a problem, too. It was not because the food was bad, but rather because it was too good. It was the best he had ever tasted in his whole life, and he had been hungry for quite a long time. He could not get rid of the nagging fear that every meal might be followed by a long famine like the hunger of those months at his grandmother's house. He stuffed himself in preparation for the famine, each time he ate, and got sick. It took a long time before he could accept the fact that food would continue to come every day, at the same time, and in abundance, like manna. Meals at Casa Materna were the first things he learned to trust.

His grandmother's continuous scolding had done one good thing for him, he found. It had given him the habit of being neat. The Pastor noticed his neatness and praised him for it. He cared for his socks every day, washing and hanging them to dry, and carefully putting them on before breakfast prayers each morning. He was a little vain about his appearance and looked at himself often in the looking glass. Sometimes the boys had to push him out of the way in order to comb their hair in the bathroom. Perhaps the house master explained to them how Roberto needed the mirror more than most people, for special reasons of his own. Perhaps they understood from their own experience how he needed to be assured that he was still himself, Roberto, by looking at himself often. The boys did not make a joke of the way Roberto stood in front of the looking glass.

About the morning prayers he had no strong feelings, nor about the evening ones, although he thought there was a good deal of worshipping at this place. Before breakfast they prayed, and before supper they all stood outside the front door of the Casa, where the Pastor faced them from the steps. He often had with him a distinguished guest, and even in his first week at Casa Materna Roberto began to understand that there were nearly always guests from far places. They made speeches in their own languages while the Pastor translated. Roberto thought the Pastor must know all the languages of the world.

Roberto, of course, had come from a Catholic home, for nearly every family in Italy is Catholic. But one would hardly have called his home religious. Crossing oneself, and genuflecting, and making novenas, for Roberto, were like tooth brushing and sock washing, not unpleasant habits. In this Protestant home he didn't cross himself, but stood at quiet attention during long prayers, and heard scripture and sang songs. Pastor Santi, who seemed to be a Protestant priest, did not dress like a priest, and there was no altar in front. The Pastor never turned his back to them to do mysterious things.

The long passionate prayers of the good Pastor sometimes might have put him to sleep if he had not been standing up with the other boys in a straight line. He did not always listen to the words, but something inside him may have listened, because there seemed to grow a connection between the Pastor's word-praying in the worship time and the music playing of the violin.

Roberto learned to waken early and to wait for the violin in the early mornings. Pastor Santi usually indulged his passion for music at dawn, after the rising time, when the music made a kind of melodic alarm, and then was almost immediately drowned in the din of children's voices all over the building.

The morning, even in December, begins early on Naples Bay, and on those frosty mornings Roberto would creep down the marble stair of the palace and stand in the shadow of the terrace, looking toward the sea, and listening while the Pastor sent his message of love and exultation to God. Sometimes the music demanded to get inside Roberto, behind the door so carefully locked to protect him from the world, even the warm little world of Casa Materna. Sometimes, though, the locked door seemed to try to crack and dissolve into the music, and then it was as if his heart were trying to break. It hurt.

But in all this listening and thinking, Roberto had steadily put off the thing he must do. Later, he told himself, always later. And all this time he was a good boy, the best of boys, and a neat boy and one who studied hard at school, and talked a great deal and ate a great deal, and grew fatter by the day and was happy.

But sometimes along after the first week of getting used to the new world, things began to happen which acted like the morning music.

94

They tried to get the door inside him unlocked. It was strange, and it hurt.

There was the time when the doctor took care of him.

He wakened that morning feeling bad, and for once did not creep down the steps to hear the violin. The sickness was a thing one does not talk about because it is a sign of weakness. Roberto could not brag about a stomach ache, if he wanted the respect of the other boys and girls. He did manage to get to breakfast, but he found that he could not eat very much even though he wanted to.

"You are not eating!" the Pastor said, reproachfully. "Your appetite, Roberto, has been so big. Is it gone now?"

He could not answer, and he could not eat. He tried to sit up straight and look dignified.

But when the line formed for marching away from breakfast, and all the boys chorused, "Arrivederci!" his legs folded up and he fell on the stone floor.

Emilio the red head was the one to speak first.

"You look green," he said, matter-of-factly. "You look ever so green!"

"I am not sick," Roberto said, firmly, and with a mighty effort he stood up again. The big room began to swim around him, and then he heard voices from a long way off, and that was all. The next time he opened his eyes he was in bed. It was not his own bed in the room with the other boys, but in the Infirmary. The nurse, Helga, was smiling at him.

He had seen the nurse before and liked her white coat, but he had not known her business. She was Swedish, and he noticed her light yellow hair and blue eyes.

"All Swedes look like that," Guilio had told him.

He liked her white coat and her smile, now when he was sick.

"Will I die?" he asked her.

"Sometime, but not now," Helga said cheerfully. "You are all right. You ate too much."

"I ate nothing at all!" he protested. "The Pastor said my appetite had gone."

"You ate too much last night, and yesterday and the night before," she said firmly.

The doctor came then, and she went away, still smiling. He decided he did not like her so much after all.

"I did not eat too much!" he insisted to Dr. Tiofilo when the doctor came in to see him a little later.

"A little, perhaps," the doctor said. "But sometimes when you go to a new place, where all the people are strange, and all things are new, you get sick. It often happens that way." The doctor took his pulse then, and nodded thoughtfully.

"Perhaps you should go to see your little sister," he said.

Roberto liked that idea, except for one thing.

"I do not wish to see my grandmother," he said. He could not mention his father, yet, or his mother. Not yet.

"Your temperature, then," said Dr. Tiofilo, and popped into Roberto's mouth a shining thing like a pencil. He could not talk for five minutes. It seemed a long time.

Maybe to be a doctor in a hospital was the best thing in the world, he thought. He went to sleep with the pencil still in his mouth, but before sleeping he had a good feeling of being cared for. It was like hearing the music, and it was like praying.

When he wakened he felt quite well and ready to go back to his own bed. The next morning he was awake at dawn and creeping down once more to listen to the violin. The ocean looked like gray lead before the sun came, and Roberto thought he had never felt so good.

That was the time when the doctor took care of him.

There was another time, in the cameo class.

Making cameos is a difficult and tedious job, as anyone knows who has ever tried to file and whittle away at a delicate shell, and to carve upon it in relief the exciting things people carve on cameos—gods and goddesses, nymphs, flowers and lovely ladies' heads.

Roberto was drawn into the small group of cameo carvers because of Emilio the red head, whose bed was next to his, and who was kind so that Roberto began to think of him as a friend, and not a stranger.

"It is fun to see something grow under your hand," Emilio told Roberto. "It is like painting a picture, only you do it with a sharp knife, and a shell."

Roberto liked the cameo teacher. He was not so sure about the knife and the shell. When he held the tiny sharp knife in his fingers they seemed suddenly big and awkward. He looked at the delicate shell with awe.

"It might break!" he said.

"Indeed, it will break if it is hurt," the teacher said. "But it is like a human life. If you handle it carefully and with love, you may make in it a beautiful picture."

Roberto examined the shell, the tool and his own clumsy fingers. Hesitantly he took up the shell and began to scratch against it. The teacher showed him how to scratch and cut and carve in the right direction.

"Your fingers will learn to speak to the shell," he explained. "They will hear and feel what the shell is answering."

Now Roberto had always known that he had two hands and needed them both for many purposes, but if anyone had asked him he would not have been able to suggest any particular thing which his hands ought to do especially well.

The first time his knife broke the shell he wanted to cry. It happened several times.

"My fingers won't do it," he said. "It is cruel, isn't it?"

"Not really," the teacher said. "It is a mistake. Your fingers will learn."

The first time Roberto finished making a picture in the shell he was happy in a way he had never known before. He looked at his own hands with wonder, and touched them together, the fingers that had made this beautiful thing.,

"This is what hands are for, I guess," he said, and felt that he had made a discovery. "Hands are to make something beautiful."

The teacher smiled.

"The hand cannot make anything more beautiful than what the heart requires of it," he said.

Roberto thought about that, and in the night, and in the early morning when he crept down to hear the violin, he wondered if perhaps this was indeed the best thing in the world—to carve cameo pictures.

So every morning the violin played. He did not always hear the words, but Roberto seemed to have some idea of what was meant.

In February, or perhaps it was as late as March, the Pastor prepared to go away to America for a long visit. Everyone knew the purpose. He would make speeches there, and play his violin, and bring back money for Casa Materna. Roberto knew, and knew that he would miss the Pastor, and the violin, in the mornings.

When the day came and the very morning when the Pastor was to go, Roberto thought that the music at dawn had a special good bye for him. It may have been special for the Pastor, too, since he was going away.

The tones of the strings went higher and higher. They would have been unbearably high, Roberto thought, and shrill, but suddenly they were not, because the high notes just missed bursting his temples and what came from the Pastor's obedient bow was so piercingly sweet that Roberto felt the tears start behind his eyes and he could hear the beating of his heart. It hurt. But he waited for it to come, and at last it came, the long, sweet note growing less and less, and ending in a quiet sigh.

Roberto was stunned. The Pastor stood silent. He seemed to be stunned, too, with the beauty of what his own hand had done.

"Buono Dio!" he whispered, aloud. Roberto echoed, or perhaps he made no sound at all, "Buono Dio!"

And then it was as though everything broke loose, and Roberto's heart broke at last. The tears pressing behind his eyes came through the lids and he could feel them hot and wet on his cheeks, like hot rain. His legs unlocked. He ran through the dark just beginning to lighten the office, and out onto the terrace that was already light. The sun, too, was breaking through the dark, and all the bay was glistening.

"Pastor Santi!" he cried, clutching the Pastor's hand.

"Roberto!" the Pastor said softly and laid the violin and bow carefully on the table. "Roberto!"

"I would like to see my father," Roberto cried.

"You will see your father," the Pastor said.

But Roberto was tugging at his hand and the Pastor bent over to hear what he would say next.

"Pastor Santi!" he said, whispering because it was so important. "When I am a man I want to be like you!"

"Like me?" The Pastor spoke with a loud strong, delighted voice. "Like me, a pastor? Many boys from Casa Materna have become ministers serving God in the church. It is good. It is very good!"

But the small hand still tugged at the big one, and Roberto stood on tip toe, to speak right into the Pastor's ear. He knew what he wanted to say. It was urgent.

"Pastor Santi, I want to be like you—a *musician*!"

The words stayed in the air waiting for the Pastor to answer. He could not speak at first, but he held the small hand tightly, and Roberto knew that there was nothing now to be afraid of. He was someone real. He could dare to give himself away. The moment he had feared so long was here, and it was good, not bad. The door he had tried to keep locked had opened in spite of him. The thinking that had to be done was done.

"I would like to see my mother!" he said. "I would like to tell her—"

But he could not see his mother. Only it would not matter because there was nothing he needed to tell her that she had not already known.

"I would like to tell my father—" he began. But his father would know, too, that everything was right between them.

"You shall see your father," the Pastor promised. "And we will talk about the music. I think there may be an instrument in America to come back with me."

The whole Bay of Naples was dazzling bright now, and the voices of the children could be heard above and around. Off to the right, Ischia could be dimly seen, and just before it the dark spot that was Puseoli. It was a long walk from there to Rome.

Behind them Vesuvius slept quietly, not threatening now, but more like a protector, or an older friend that you might talk to about many things.

The Pastor

All that day the Pastor sat in the jet plane that sped fast over Europe. Departing in the bright morning of Naples, he continued in the bright day of Paris and London, and on toward the still bright day of New York. Flying in the light! There was a sermon in that, he thought.

He thought of Roberto.

The boy must have come to terms with himself.

"This is what I prayed for!" the Pastor said to himself, not realizing that he spoke aloud.

The woman in the aisle seat opened her eyes.

"I beg your pardon?" she inquired.

The Pastor smiled at her.

"This was my son that was dead and is alive!" he explained. It was all beginning to be clear to him.

The woman looked not so much puzzled as awed, as one sometimes is in church when a mystery is recognized and accepted. But the Pastor was careful after that to think silently, for he could not talk about this miracle.

The boy had made a commitment, not to the ministry, but to music. It was a little disappointing, for Casa Materna had produced many ministers, distinguished men of God.

And a musician! The Pastor knew too well what that meant. Hard long years of work, probably without any real success or recognition at the end. And he had hardly any notion of whether or not Roberto really had this gift from God. Perhaps his gift was to receive the music, not create it. There might be heartbreak! The Pastor himself had the gift of creating. He knew that. And what then about a creator musician like himself, who had answered another call, and laid aside the music for another ministry? Had it been right? Well, it had been necessary!

Was it too great a sacrifice to yearn for all the rest of one's life for the lost chord?

He stirred restlessly in his seat.

"Into thy hand, Signore!" he said, and went to sleep then, still flying into the continuing light.

9. The End is the Beginning

Most of the writings about Casa Materna have begun with its thrilling history. We have preferred to start off in the present, and to offer as a sort of epilogue the marvelous story of how it all began. It is appropriate that these little stories of some "miracles at Portici" conclude with the great miracle which made the stories possible. Here is the story of Casa Materna!

On October 22, 1905, Pastor Riccardo Santi, a young Methodist preacher in Naples, had a remarkable experience. It happened on his birthday, when he was out walking, recalling other birthdays, and all the days of his own life since his orphaned childhood, and thinking how he had been unusually blessed in many ways. He had a good enough home, a loving wife who shared his calling, and two handsome children, a boy and a girl, rather more gifted than the average, he thought. And he had work that he loved, because it was in the service of the Lord, for whom Pastor Santi had a personal, passionate and complete devotion. Like most preachers he was not rich in this world's goods, but he had far more than riches.

While thinking these thoughts, and not forgetting to thank God for his blessings, Pastor Riccardo Santi came upon two poor children, a sick little boy and his ragged sister who were selling matches in the great archway of Naples.

"Why are you selling matches?" he asked them.

"We sell matches to buy food," the little boy said. "Our mother is sick and our father is dead and there is no money unless we sell matches."

"Do you sell very many?" Pastor Santi asked.

"Alas, Signore," the boy confessed, "We have not sold three lira's worth this morning. Every gentleman who passes this corner, it seems, has no need for matches."

Then a strange thing happened. Out of the blue sky there came a voice.

"Take them and love them for my sake," the voice said to the young Pastor. "As it was done to you, do you also unto these little ones."

Pastor Santi believed at once that the voice came from the Lord, and he was used to obeying God without asking questions. He took the two children straight home to his wife.

"Who are they?" Signora Santi asked her husband.

"I have not asked their names," he told her. "But they are ours to care for as I was cared for when I was an orphan child."

Now Signora Santi, who had her household to provide for out of Pastor Santi's small pay, and two young Santis already who were always hungry and wearing out their shoe soles, was not so sure about the voice. But she was very sure of her husband, and they took the children. They also found a place in the hospital for the children's mother, who blessed them for making a home for her little ones.

There wasn't enough room at the Santis' home, but Louisa who was four years old gave the sick girl half of her small bed, and Emanuele, who was six, gave the boy half of his bed, and they managed that way. There wasn't enough food, either, which was more serious. Louisa gave half her oatmeal every morning to the little girl, and Emanuele shared his with the boy. But by Sunday morning there were four hungry children instead of two full ones.

"We have not enough food," Signora said firmly to her husband. "You will have to do something."

On that Sunday morning Pastor Santi took for his text the Scripture verse, "Inasmuch as ye have done it unto one of the least of these, ye have done it unto Me," and he told his little congregation about the children and the voice.

That very afternoon things began to happen. A chair and another bed appeared right out in front of the door to the Santi house. Clothes—trousers, shirts, dresses and shoes, appeared. Potatoes came, and spaghetti and beans. Until late at night the Pastor and his wife kept going to answer knocks at the door, and finding parcels there.

"We have too much food!" said the Pastor. "We have more beds than we can use. We can have more children here!"

103

There were many orphan children in Naples then, as now, and the Santis took another and another and another child into the home until presently there were six. Then there were ten, and finally there were fifty living in the house that had been just big enough for four! But still there were homeless children in Naples.

The Santis and their family were crowded. They never had quite enough money, but they managed. Not only did they make a home for the children but they also started a school for them. All this happened in one house.

By that time several years had gone by and nobody outside had paid much attention except Pastor Santi's loyal little congregation. But one day, in the year 1919, some visitors came from America. There were five men in a big automobile. They were Methodists who had heard about the orphanage with fifty children at Portici, all jammed together with a school in one house.

"Frankly," they said to Pastor Santi, "we do not approve of children being crowded. In America it is not done this way. We advise you to close your orphanage."

"There is more room in the streets than in this house," Pastor Santi agreed. "But I ask you to have a look around before you make up your mind to advise me. First, please, look at the street."

They looked at the street which was dirty and crowded as well. The children out there were dirty, too, and some of them were sick

The visitors then began to look around them *inside* the house, and they stayed all of one morning to look. In the dining room and living room, which each morning were converted into schoolrooms, the children crowded closer together to make room for the five big men. In the bedrooms they saw fifty little beds, double deckers close together, but each one made up with its own small blanket and sheet.

"It is better than no bed at all, is it not?" Pastor Santi asked.

They ate at noon the clean food, the bread and the spaghetti.

"It is not much, but it is better than nothing, and it is clean," the Pastor said.

They heard the children sing.

"Only happy children sing," Pastor Santi reminded them. "And only healthy children can sing with such loud voices."

When it was time for them to go, the leader of the visitors spoke.

"We have changed our opinion," he said. "We advise you not to close this home. And we will give you some money for the children. How much do you want?"

"I don't want money," Pastor Santi told them.

A Methodist preacher not wanting money? Incredible!

"Then what do you want?" they asked.

"I want a new house," he told them. "I want a house with a garden where they can dig, and a place for a workshop and a school building. And I want a place where they can play."

That shocked the visitors because a house big enough to hold all those children, with a garden and a playground besides, was quite a large request.

"We will take it under consideration," they said finally. Then they rode away in the big automobile.

When her husband told her about all this, Signora Santi was chagrined.

"Those men will forget!" she exclaimed. "You should have taken the money when they offered it."

"The men might forget, it is true," said Pastor Santi. "But the Lord will not."

Days and weeks and finally a month and two months went by and they heard nothing from America.

"You see, they have forgotten," Signora Santi told her husband. "You were wrong to trust the Methodists. They are too busy."

"The Lord will not forget," Pastor Santi said again. And that very day he received three more children whose parents had died far south in Calabria province, and who had come alone, walking all that long way to Naples. There were now fifty-three children in the family.

One day, at long last, the same big automobile drove up to the door of the Santi home and the same five men were in it. But only one of them got out this time. It was the leader who came to the door. Pastor Santi invited him inside, but he said they were very busy and there was no time for visiting.

105

"We have come to take you with us to buy a new house for your children," he said.

Pastor Santi did not stop even to go back and get his hat. He called through the window to tell his wife that he was going with the men in the automobile to buy a house, and then they started.

They rode all over Naples. They looked at every house that was marked for sale. But there was something wrong with all of them. Some were too small, some were too dark, some were all right except that they had no room in the back for a garden. Pastor Santi especially requested a garden where the children could dig.

Just when they thought that perhaps they would not find in all of Naples exactly the right kind of house for the children, the driver brought them to the big estate in Portici, by the sea. It was the house which had belonged to the Prince of Monaco years before. And besides the palace, there was a second building, and there was a wide beach where the prince and his friends in the old days came to bathe. Best of all, better even than the beach, there was between the two buildings a beautiful garden with wide walks and palm trees and fountains and statues. It was the most beautiful place in the world for princes and for children.

Pastor Santi looked at the beach and the garden and the two big buildings. He did not say a word.

"How will this do?" the leader asked him.

"It is exactly right," Pastor Santi said. "But it will cost a good deal of money."

"You shall have it," the leader said.

Through all the years that followed, Pastor Santi continued to preach to his little congregation in the Naples church, and most of them were loyal and good, but sometimes there were disappointments. Once a certain man grew angry because he thought that one of the Pastor's sermons was directed against him, and so Signore Giardi simply never came back to the church. That hurt the Pastor a good deal, for he loved every one of his flock, as he called them.

In Casa Materna, too, there were problems. Living in a palace meant that there was more room, and there were therefore more children, and more mouths to feed. There was one evening when they had not another box of oatmeal in the palace, and there was no knowing where breakfast would come from.

"Well, I will sell the living room couch," Signora Santi said. "It will bring enough for one meal, perhaps, and then—"

"The Lord will provide," said Pastor Santi. "Let us pray before going to the evening service."

While they were praying there was a knock on the door of the room at the top of the stairs, and then they heard the sound of feet running away. Pastor Santi went to the door but no one was there, only an envelope lay on the floor. When he opened it he found a fifty lira note inside.

"There is enough money for breakfast," said Pastor Santi. "And you may keep the couch for another time."

"Who sent the money?" asked his wife.

"The Lord sent the money," said Pastor Santi. "I do not know who brought it." But he looked again in the envelope and found a paper which read, "Forgive my trespasses." That night Signore Giardi was at church. After the service, Signora Santi said to her husband, "It was Giardi who sent the money, I think."

"I think it was the Lord," the Pastor repeated.

As the years went by there were two more Santi children added to the family, and all of the four grew up among the other children in the bigger family. When the time came for them to choose their careers in the world, Fabio, the youngest son, decided to become a lawyer, because he thought so large a family would surely need the service of the law. Tiofilo, the middle son, studied medicine, because with so many children a doctor would surely be needed. Emanuele studied music and became a distinguished violinist, but he also studied to be a minister like his father, and went to preach in America. Louisa for many years helped her mother to run the household and taught in the school, before she, too, went to America.

People were not always kind. Some became jealous of the Pastor's big family and tried to keep the orphanage from operating. Others started other orphanages and schools in order to take care of more children. That pleased the Pastor. "There are far more homeless children in Naples than Casa Materna can provide for," he said. "If we have encouraged others to help us in the big job, then we should have a Casa Materna in every city of Italy."

When Mussolini came to power in Italy he ordered the home to close its doors. But by this time Fabio Santi was an experienced lawyer, and he fought that case right through the courts all the way to Rome, where he won it for Casa Materna, even against Il Duce himself. Casa Materna was not closed, not for one day.

World War II brought Casa Materna frightful problems. Since Portici was close to the harbor, and also to the railway center, that city was mercilessly bombed, and Casa Materna was bombed along with the rest of Portici.

The air raids were terrible times for the leaders of the home, but the children rather enjoyed them. As soon as they heard the sirens, the children were led into bomb shelters down under the palace, and there they sang and sang—songs like, "God will take care of you," and "Are we downhearted? No, no, no!" There was not much food, but Signora Santi saved a little bit of jam for those times, and whenever there was a raid they had a party down in the shelter while the bombs whistled over their heads. Whenever they heard the siren, the younger children thought it meant a party.

The parties ended after one bomb destroyed the big building by the sea, and all the children had to be taken to a village outside Naples where they stayed until the fighting was over. Not only Casa Materna, but the whole of Portici was in ruins. Many people had gone to caves outside the city where they made shift to stay alive. After the war was ended, the Santi family and the children returned to occupy the shambles of the old palace.

American bombs destroyed Casa Materna. It is good, then, to be able to report that American soldiers helped to rebuild the home. During the occupation many soldiers were quartered near the site where the old building had been. These man spent their free time there with the children and learned to love them. Many wrote back to their homes and to churches they knew in the United States, to ask for help for Casa Materna. The response was generous enough so that in the end they raised enough money to have the building by the sea entirely rebuilt.

Today two big visitors' books in the office record the names of the American young men who had a part in the new life of Casa Materna.

Following the war and the occupation and for many years after that, the new needs of children in this stricken country filled the home with children whose parents had been killed, or lost in the war, and with children whose fathers were never known at all. For every boy and girl who came, alone and bereft, to find refuge at Casa Materna, Pastor Santi had the same words: "When a child comes to me for help I do not ask if that child suffers. I become the child."

Mama Santi departed this life in 1956, and it seemed as though her going marked the beginning of a whole era of sad years for Casa Materna. The following year Fabio Santi, who was directing the home by this time, was driving to Rome, wrecked his car and died in the crash. It was the greatest tragedy that has ever come to Casa Materna. Both Tiofilo and Emanuele always declared that Fabio was the most able of all the family. I knew him from an early visit, and will always remember his great size and strength, and his incredible gentleness. It was touching to see that stunning young giant defer so tenderly and respectfully to his father, who was small of stature, although so mighty in spirit.

Emanuele came home to join his brother Tiofilo, and his aged father, after that. It was a sad homecoming, and just what it meant to him to leave a distinguished career in music which he loved, and a thriving church in New York, it is hard to say. The Santi family have never measured their lives in terms of costs and sacrifices. They have done what needed doing. Emanuele Santi was needed, and he returned home.

Papa Santi left them in 1962. He was in his eighties by that time, but still alert and active. I came back for one of my visits that same spring, only a short time after the funeral which had been one of the largest in the history of Portici and Naples. The posters eulogizing the Pastor were still bravely plastering the walls outside the gates, for this is the custom in Italy when a great leader dies.

Today Emanuele, the Pastor, and Tiofilo the doctor, work together. As I have tried to show in these stories, Naples and Portici grow and change continuously, bringing bigger problems every day.

The Casa Materna school has for years been known as the best in Portici and one of the best in the Naples area. The home continues to seek and serve homeless children and to restore broken families to each other. Young people from all over Europe and from America come to serve on the staff.

There is always an international air about the place, and the children grow accustomed to hearing many languages spoken around them.

Pressures from the government are not as great now as in the early days, because of the relaxed attitude of the Roman church. Father Borelli, the well-known priest and social leader, is an associate of the Santi brothers. But even so, there is no financial support from the state for the Protestant school and home, and there is always the danger of financial disaster. Casa Materna's endurance in the face of every kind of discouragement and loss is a continuing miracle.

This tough quality about the home seems not quite consistent with the fragile, almost dreamlike beauty of its buildings. And yet the structure has a certain permanence, too. The same grace one associates with the Coliseum, or the Forum, or the magnificent excavations of Pompeii and Herculaneum, describes the Pompeian red palace of Casa Materna, and the fountains and formal planting of its gardens. If that irresponsible monster Vesuvius were to begin belching forth lava and brimstone next summer, as it did as late as 1949, all the way to Portici, and even if it should bury this home in lava dust, one would wait confidently for it to dig itself out and emerge, rosy and graceful again.

But of course, as Papa Santi might say, the buildings are only outward signs of an inward grace. This home could not really come to an end because there would always be the lives of the children who have been there, and their children after them, and all the others whom the home has touched and changed. These would always stand for Casa Materna. And this is surely the kind of permanence Papa Santi would want.